Victorian Farms

Victorian Farms

ROY BRIGDEN

The Crowood Press

First published in 1986 by
THE CROWOOD PRESS
Ramsbury, Marlborough,
Wiltshire SN8 2HE

British Library Cataloguing in Publication Data

Brigden, Roy
Victorian farms.
1. Agriculture —— Great Britain —— History —— 19th century
I. Title
630′.941   S455

ISBN 0-946284-66-0

Picture Credits

The photograph on the front of the jacket and those on
pages 77, 84 and 85 are reproduced by gracious permission
of Her Majesty the Queen.

All site photographs are by the author. The remainder
are the copyright of The Institute of Agricultural
History and Museum of English Rural Life, University
of Reading.

The line illustrations on pages 38, 61 and 72 are by
Godfrey Eke.

Typeset by Alacrity Phototypesetters, Weston-super-Mare

Printed and bound in Great Britain by
Robert Hartnoll (1985) Ltd.,
Bodmin Cornwall

Contents

Acknowledgements

This book could not have been written without generous help from the many farmers and landowners who have made me very welcome in the course of my roamings around the English countryside over the last few years. For fear of omitting some names, I will not attempt to list them individually but my gratitude applies equally to all. No one has turned me away or taken offence at my professional inquisitiveness and almost everywhere I have found a genuine interest in the past that gives the lie to some of the more lurid popular images of the modern commercial farmer. It must be said, however, that nearly all the sites mentioned and illustrated here are private property with no rights of general access, so for this reason precise details of location have been withheld.

Thanks must go also to my colleagues at Reading for their frequent and valuable assistance; special thanks to Barbara and the Photographic Service for the processing of my requests with much patient efficiency, and to Phyllis and Helen for doing so well with the typing.

Lastly a word of appreciation for my wife Tricia, young James and baby Tom, born during Chapter 8, who have been so tolerant of my long absences in the study or on the road.

ROY BRIGDEN
Three Mile Cross
December 1985

Introduction

Nineteenth-century England with its multiplying population represented both a challenge and a threat to the Victorian farmer. On the one hand, more mouths to feed and more money to spend on a more varied diet stimulated new developments in food production, using all the assistance that science and technology could offer; but, on the other, urban interests were becoming decisive both politically and economically and would not be showing the farmer any special favours. The townsman would have his food at the lowest possible price and from wherever in the world it could be obtained, irrespective of the effect this might have on the producer at home. Agricultural fortunes rose and fell in consequence as mid-century confidence in the supreme bounty of progress was later bludgeoned into near-despair by an overwhelming flood of cheap imports from fresh young territories overseas. In the course of it all, Victorian farming made its indelible mark and created the agricultural landscape that forms the subject of this book.

The chapters that follow have as a common thread the achievements of Victorian agriculture, the dramatic changes they wrought upon the face of the countryside and some of the leading figures associated with them. It is not intended to be read as a straightforward history for the emphasis mostly ignores the typical in order to concentrate entirely on the new trends and breakthroughs, of which there were so many over the duration of the reign. The primary raw material is provided by the surviving physical evidence in the field collected in the course of many journeys of discovery and exploration into the rural past. What emerges is a glimpse of the very real tangible presence of the Victorian era upon the countryside of today, which, once recognised, can be identified everywhere – in the layout of the field, the line of a hedge and the buildings of farmstead and village. They are just as much the Victorian farmer's memorial as the ploughs and seed drills, the reapers and threshing machines which helped to carve the new agricultural environment and are now to be found in museums and collections all over the country.

Queen Victoria: symbol of the age, 1837–1901.

The home farm at Berkeley Castle, Gloucestershire, built
in the late 1850s. In the middle distance is the former
steam-powered threshing area with a sawmill adjacent.

All these aspects are manifestations of change brought about by
the need to adjust farming operations to the different demands being
made by a rapidly evolving industrial society. Quite a lot of the so-
called traditional elements of the countryside that are fiercely
defended today are not simply man-made but are less than 150 years
old. The miles of hedgerow that were grubbed up in the 1850s and
1860s to create larger fields for bigger machinery to work in, the
number of old buildings that were swept aside to make way for new
types of farm complex, and the tonnages of chemical fertiliser that
were applied to the soil in the pursuit of higher yields would no doubt
raise a few eyebrows amongst the late twentieth-century conservation movement. This is not to undermine the case for protection
but to set it within the context of a dynamic countryside, characterised by change, rather than trying to pin it to fixed points of reference
that do not in reality exist. The course of farming was not governed

Egmere Farm on the Holkham estate in Norfolk
now restored to a sound condition.

by some ancient and immutable lore of primitive practice that was
suddenly and irreversibly overtaken in 1900, 1950, or whenever, by
the power of modern commercialism. More accurate is a picture of
constant movement where today's progress is tomorrow's tradition
and where both elements may usually be found side by side. Here lies
the key to Victorian farming, for while it retained many links with
preceding centuries it also, in no small way, nurtured a great agri-
business of the future through its early stages of growth. The more
the countryside is studied and interpreted on this basis, the more
informed will the debate about its protection and survival become.

No one needs to be reminded of the scale and pace of change at
present affecting the natural environment, whether caused by agricultural reorganisation, industrial development or continued urban
expansion. During the writing of this book at least one of the sites
illustrated has been obliterated and another two changed out of all
recognition in the name of improvement. Although only a bare

Working horse stables at Egmere Farm.

scraping of the surface can be given here of the many riches that do still remain, nevertheless the rate at which sites can and do disappear, notwithstanding legislative protection, must be of concern. On the credit side of the equation, however, there are cases that give grounds for hope and encouragement. Take, for example, Egmere Farm on the Holkham estate in Norfolk, built in the early 1850s by George Dean, a major exponent of the industrialised agriculture of the period, of whom more later. In the late 1970s, the steading was redundant and semi-derelict with the prospect before it of further steady decay towards ruin. Since then, it has come back from the brink: buildings have been reroofed and made watertight, tumble-down brickwork made good and the debris of neglect removed. More important, perhaps, agricultural usage has been retained for at least part of the site while the remainder is left alone in a state of suspended animation. Another approach, prompted by different circumstances, may be seen at work on the Oxfordshire estate based on the hamlets of Ardington and Lockinge. Here the exploitation of non-

Cattle fattening house at Egmere with separate fattening
cubicles or boxes, each with a sunken floor for the
containment of manure, on either side of a central
feeding passage.

agricultural sources of income and the fostering of alternative sources
of employment have been adopted as means of preserving the viability
of the estate and of defending the vitality of its dependent village
community against the encroachment of a commuter invasion. An
essential part of the process has been the protection, through conversion to commercial and light industrial use, of much of the stock of
Victorian buildings constructed on the estate by the first Lord
Wantage. It is worth remembering, therefore, that the role of the
enlightened landlord and farmer, such a pronounced feature of the
nineteenth-century countryside, lives on and will remain crucially
important.

Going by previous years, the immediate outlook for the farmer in
1837, at the beginning of Victoria's reign, was not too bright.
Economic recession had quickly followed the ending in 1815 of the
Napoleonic wartime boom and its shock waves were felt far through-

The home farm on the Westonbirt estate in Gloucestershire,
built in the mid-1850s, with the main processing block
in the centre.

out the system. Sluggish corn prices and falling land values produced
bankruptcy and distress amongst farmers accompanied by unemploy-
ment and unrest amongst the labour force. Areas of marginal land
that had been optimistically ploughed during the war reverted to
rough pasture or waste and speculation in new techniques and
technology, so marked during the years of prosperity, was replaced
by the siege mentality of survival. Yet, in spite of the pain, the process
of adapting to the peace did induce a degree of deck-clearing that was
an important preliminary to subsequent development.

Three measures may be singled out. In 1834, a new Poor Law was
introduced with a revised structure of social assistance, albeit meagre,
issuing through separate combinations of parishes, or unions, supervised in each case by a board of guardians. There was little dignity or
compassion in a regime that forced the poor, the sick and the old
either to stand on their own feet or face the humiliation and
degradation of the workhouse. Rationalisation had to come, how-

ever, for the countryside was sinking beneath the absurdities of a system that imposed crippling rates for the purpose of subsidising the inadequate wages of those in work. Two years later, pressure of circumstance tackled another vexed question when an Act of Commutation converted the tithe from payment in kind to a straight financial transaction based on a formula linked to the price of corn. Even so, the burden was still to be borne by the tenant farmer, in whom this tax on efficiency aroused considerable resentment, for payment was not transferred to owners of land until 1891. All the while, the aftermath of the long process of fundamental change in the management and administration of the agricultural landscape was taking its course. The war had prompted another peak in the move to enclose the remaining areas of open land, with 2,000 individual Acts of Enclosure making their way through Parliament, and the process continued, though at a much reduced rate, for some decades yet. Along the way, many of the lingering accretions of custom, and logistical encumbrances to effective farming, were swept aside, to be replaced by the common pattern of consolidated holdings held under tenancy from a single landlord.

Standing out like an agricultural landmark from the early years of Victoria's reign was the repeal in 1846 of protective measures on the price of corn. Although the disastrous famine in Ireland was an immediate spur, it was a move that indirectly embraced much wider political and constitutional issues and signalled another stage in the evolution of a trading nation. A free market for food would, so the argument ran, mean more money in the pockets of the populace to spend on consumer goods and would encourage further reciprocal trading links with the principal food-exporting countries. The farming community viewed the matter rather differently and was thrown into a panic that appeared all the more justified by a significant drop in the price of grain from 1848 through to 1852. Fears of doom, however, were not realised, at least for the time being, for there followed a quarter-century of comparative stability and prosperity that was subsequently looked back upon as a Golden Age. It was not that the predicted growth in food imports did not happen but rather that the effects of population expansion continued to allow the home farmer a competitive access to the domestic market. In this he was helped by the emerging infrastructure of a manufacturing economy: the new rail networks and the steam shipping companies provided

House with buildings for horses and implements dating
from the 1850s at Stanley Farm, then part of the
Duke of Beaufort's estate, near Bristol.

quick and easy facilities for the transport of produce from the
country to the town and the joint-stock banks offered a means of
ironing out some of the peaks and troughs in his annual cash flow. A
period, broadly speaking, of favourable harvests was also significant,
as was the absence of great political or armed conflict on a scale
witnessed by some other European countries.

In the uncertain years of the late 1840s, changes designed to
cushion the impact of the free trade policy could be seen under way
on many farms. Returning confidence quickly bred more investment
in improved methods to boost output not only in terms of volume
but of productivity and quality as well. Here was the beginning of the
doctrine of 'high farming' which so characterised the prevailing tone
of these years and which lies behind much of the innovation described
in this book. Not all farmers or landowners were enthused and there
were those who remained unconvinced of the ability of money and
the new ways to work the expected miracles. Nevertheless, over the

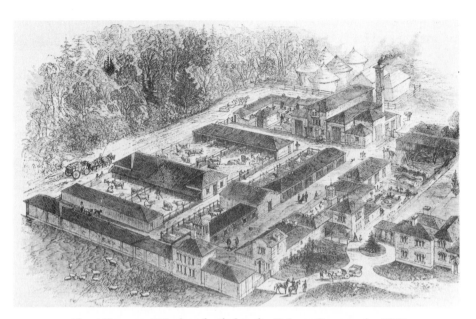

Shaw Farm at Windsor built by the Prince Consort in 1853
and designed by G. A. Dean. The house for the farm manager,
at the right, included a suite of rooms for the Queen
from where she could gain private access to the farmstead
via the poultry buildings.

country as a whole the total spend was colossal. Efficient field
drainage, particularly for those cold, wet clay lands that had suffered
the brunt of the earlier depression, was an early target made even
more attractive by the availability of government grants. It was
accompanied by increasing outlays on fertiliser such as bones and
Peruvian guano, on new and better equipped farmsteads to replace
the inconvenient leftovers from pre-enclosure times, and on more
sophisticated and labour-saving equipment to counteract the drift of
manpower away from the rural districts in search of more lucrative
employment in the towns. There was further work, too, on the
livestock front, with the continuing consolidation and extension of
improvements, already in train for many years, to replace the general-
purpose farm animal with more specialist and efficient stock
supplying beef, mutton and pork of the taste and texture popularly
demanded.

It was an era of progress across a very broad front in which the business of farming began to appear more professional and systematic to society at large. One example of this was the creation in 1866 of a system for the regular collection of national statistics covering all aspects of agricultural output; another was the accumulation of experimental data by researchers in their efforts to promote a fuller scientific understanding of crop growth and livestock production. The Royal Agricultural Society, founded under a slightly different name in 1838, reached the peak of its influence during these years by fostering and disseminating innovation wherever it was to be found. Its motto 'Practice with Science' aptly summarised the spirit of inquiry that was abroad and its journal was a focal point of expression not only for leading farmers but for an emerging array of experts – from architects and engineers to chemists, botanists and soil scientists – who had staked an interest in the health and prosperity of the agricultural industry. The organisation was not without its critics, but there could be few English agriculturalists or landlords of distinction who were not involved in the Society's affairs one way or another, through membership of one of its specialist committees, contributions to the journal, or official duties at the annual show. The royal family itself was closely associated, for Victoria remained the Society's patron from 1840 to her death, and both she and the Prince Consort, as well as the Prince of Wales, served terms as president. At Windsor, the extensive works carried out on the royal farms in the middle of the century brought the widest publicity and, above all, made agricultural improvement fashionable.

The abrupt deterioration in fortunes that set in from the mid-1870s began with a series of below-par harvests culminating, in 1879, with one of the wettest and most dismal seasons it was possible to imagine. At the same time, a world-wide recession hit Britain harder than most and its effect upon domestic agriculture was made much worse by the full force of cheap grain imports from new lands overseas, particularly in the American West, that had recently been brought into productive cultivation. The distress this caused was severe for those who in the previous decades had committed themselves so heartily to a commodity they could no longer sell for a satisfactory price. Another painful process of adjustment was called for, bringing with it a fall in land values, a reduction in rents and a contraction of the national corn acreage. In its place, more land was

Shacklewell Lodge Farm near Empingham in Leicestershire,
built in the early 1870s.

turned over to market gardens and orchards and there was a much
greater emphasis on livestock production and dairying. There was
some security in liquid milk, the urban demand for which could be
met only by the farmer at home, but meat prices could not be
maintained once the new refrigerated ships had begun in the 1880s to
exploit the potential of moving low-cost beef and mutton from the
other side of the world.

By the end of the reign, the worst of the depression was over and
the general state of shock was dispersing. Those farmers who survived
had done so by making the most of the remaining market opportunities available, introducing stringent cost-cutting measures and
coming to terms with the realities of the new economic environment.
The State had not been totally unmoved by the conditions of
agricultural distress and had passed some legislation designed to
make life a little easier without budging an inch on the fundamental
policy of free trade. Even agricultural circles now recognised that
there could be little hope of the principles of that policy being altered
when the country was so heavily dependent upon foreign food
supplies to feed its population. For the pragmatic farmer, the only

Former village iron foundry, equipped with both water and
steam power, at Bucklebury in Berkshire. In the nineteenth
century it was run by the Hedges family and counted
agricultural equipment, including waterwheels for some
neighbouring farms, amongst its products.

Twin cylinder portable steam engine suitable for farm use
by Ransomes and Sims, photographed at the firm's
Orwell Works in Ipswich in the 1860s.

practical alternative was to get by as best he could and this is what many did. The countryside bore all the marks of this change and decline, not least in the 2 million acres that had reverted from arable to pasture. On many holdings, buildings, fences and farm roads deteriorated from lack of maintenance and both the labour force and the rural community as a whole suffered through the continuous draining away of its younger and healthier members to the towns. It would take a world war for the importance of a vigorous domestic agricultural industry to be recognised once more, however briefly.

1
Farm Buildings

Nowhere is the agricultural legacy of the Victorian period more pronounced than in the area of farm buildings. Over the first half-century of the reign, construction of new farmsteads, and modernisation of existing ones, was a consuming interest for those landlords who were of an improving mind. Later on, into the 1880s and 1890s, the economics of depression served to dampen the ardour, yet even so examples can be found of further investment in buildings, particularly livestock accommodation, as a reaction to the changing agricultural climate. The Victorians, of course, did not invent farmstead design. In the eighteenth century, too, a good deal of attention had been devoted to the subject as a result of which basic conventions of layout were established. On the eve of the Victorian period J.C. Loudon's *Encyclopaedia of Agriculture* introduced an extensive section of farm plans and analyses with the words, 'there is nothing which marks more decidedly the state of agriculture in any district, than the plan and execution of these buildings'.[1] So the Victorian boom in new farmstead construction, with the peak period spanning the years 1850–70, drew upon existing ideas with a renewed vigour, added some more, and raised farm architecture to the level of a science.

MOTIVES FOR BUILDING

There were a number of reasons for this emphasis on building work. The complete relocation of a farmstead might be desirable following enclosure if the existing buildings were in an inconvenient position relative to the rest of the holding. Notwithstanding the improvements that had already been made in some areas, farms were commonly made up of an amalgam of buildings that had accumulated over the centuries to no logical plan, were unsuited to present conditions and were, in any case, falling into disrepair. It was this that

23

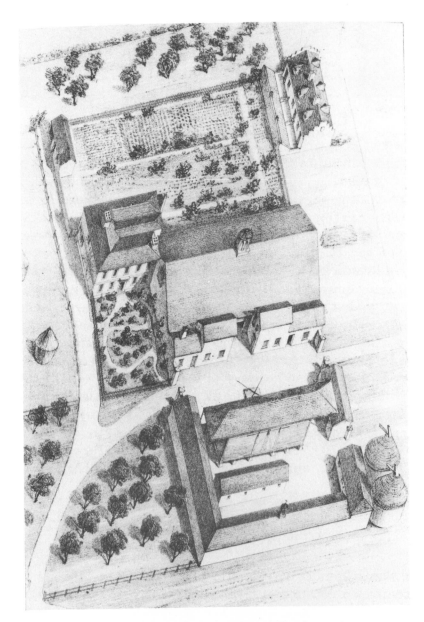

West Peckham Farm from Lord Torrington's
On Farm Buildings, 1845. Just visible is the
fixed horse gear sited in the central courtyard
to drive feed preparing machinery in the store houses
in front of the cattle lodge on one side and the
threshing machine in the wooden barn on the other.

prompted James Caird, after his tour of England in 1851, to talk of 'inconvenient, ill-arranged hovels'[2] and J.C. Morton to describe the typical farmstead where 'uncheered by a ray of sunshine, wading in a pool of rain water from the roofs of buildings, and of liquid manure from the houses, the stock was suffered to languish'.[3] The feeling was that improvements made elsewhere on the farm, including field drainage, new breeds of stock and more sophisticated equipment, were likely to be negated by inadequate buildings at the farmstead itself.

With manufacturing industry thrusting ahead in mid-century, a potent source of comparison was provided between the factory, with its efficient arrangement of production to economise on time and labour, and the farmstead, with its traditional muddle and waste. Viscount Torrington, who in 1845 redesigned a farm on his estate at West Peckham in Kent, was one of many who made this point.[4] If it was right for the manufacturer, then the farmer should similarly be equipped with buildings that conserved material and manpower and made use of appropriate machinery to increase productivity. He also cited another common example of the mainline railway station, where 'everything is placed for the required occasion' and where the superintendent could see all that was going on from a strategically sited office. This is probably why the West Peckham farmstead was, curiously, built on to an already existing house, for a window in the adjoining wall gave the farmer a commanding view from his sitting-room into the cattle lodge.

The form and layout of buildings at West Peckham reflected Torrington's view that the whole site should be lockable at night, that too much open space led to untidiness and that large barns were an unnecessarily expensive appendage. Unthreshed corn was stored in individual stacks in a separate yard nearby so that the wooden barn here needed only to house the contents of a single stack, together with the horse-driven threshing machinery and some of the resulting straw. Over fifty cattle could be accommodated, most of them in the large building adjacent to the house where the fatting beasts were tied to posts set in the rows of brick mangers. From these standings the liquid manure drained away to an underground tank while the dung was collected at periodic intervals by a boy and removed to an open storage yard outside. One of the guiding principles of the day was clearly in operation here: that warmth is the equivalent of food. In

The wooden barn at West Peckham raised up on
staddle-stones and with its fixed threshing machine
in the middle receiving power from the
four-horse gear outside.

Inside the cattle lodge at West Peckham. The little window
from the sitting-room in the house adjacent can be seen
on the end wall. A single span roof for the 54ft
wide building allowed for maximum internal
ventilation. Air was also ducted into the double
lines of brick mangers and vented at each standing
through the openings shown.

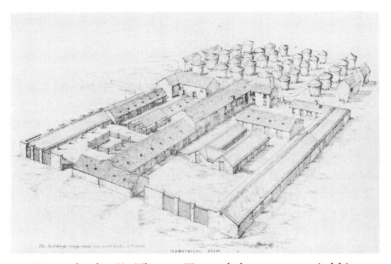

Farm plan by Sir Thomas Tancred that accompanied his
Prize Essay on farm buildings for the Royal Agricultural
Society in 1850. The design proceeds from a stackyard,
equipped with a tramway, to a steam-powered processing
house and on down through a central line of cattle
fattening boxes flanked on either side by accommodation
for sheep and pigs. From the *JRASE* of that year.

other words, the more an animal was protected from the elements,
the more flesh and fat it would put on from a given quantity of food.
Other features of the design, however, reflect its comparatively early
date. A decade later, for example, the stackyard would not have been
so remote, the arrangement of machinery would have been more
integrated and the manure storage facilities probably more elaborate.

West Peckham, then, was a product of the growing interest
spreading through the agricultural community. In tune with this
feeling, the Royal Agricultural Society organised a prize essay competition on the subject of farm buildings in 1850. It was the opinion
of H. S. Thompson, one of the judges, that 'never since the formation
of the Society were so many good reports sent in for one prize'[5] and
their publication in the journal was a significant contribution both
to general principles and to more precise details of arrangement and
construction. Thereafter, the specimen plans and descriptions of
farmsteads which frequently appeared in this and other relevant
journals gave expression to new ideas or opinions and served to keep
the discussion flowing.

27

THE PURSUIT OF EFFICIENCY

Perhaps the real debate, however, was not so much on the printed page but on those many farms around the country where new sets of buildings were being constructed and theory put into practice. Whether these were principally dairy, stock-rearing or arable farms, the objective in every case was to find the right formula of building type and arrangement to achieve maximum effectiveness and efficiency. Each farm type embraced a variety of operations. Dairy farms, for example, would typically keep pigs to feed off the milk by-products and, like the more exclusively stock-rearing farms, were likely to have part of their acreage under fodder crops. Livestock, on the other hand, were an important element in the corn-growing arable farms. They would consume the root crops grown as part of the normal rotation, together with any bought-in feed, and convert them and the straw litter into valuable manure that went back on the fields to maintain them in good, fertile condition. It was in the buildings of the farmstead itself that the mutually dependent activities came together. Here the equipment was housed, the crops and feed were processed and stored, the livestock accommodated, the manure produced and the meat and dairy products prepared for market. It followed, then, that the layout and specification of the buildings could have a significant influence upon both the level and quality of output as well as the amount, and therefore cost, of the labour involved.

It was a feature of the middle decades of the nineteenth century that the willingness was there to invest in this kind of productivity increase. High farming, the prevailing agricultural philosophy of the day, provided the encouragement by vigorously advising the maximising of investment in order to correspondingly maximise returns. For G. H. Andrews, a total believer:

'high farming is economy of labour and manure, and plenty of both. Now the economy of labour and manure, in reference to stock, will depend principally upon the judicious arrangement of the sheds, hammels, courts etc for the better supply of food, removal of dung and preservation of the liquid manure ...'[6]

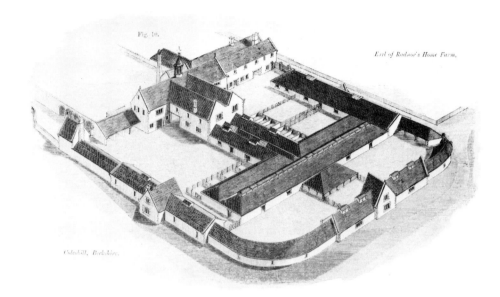

Coleshill Farm from *The Farmer's Calendar*, 1862. The
stackyard is at the top left, giving on to the steam-powered
processing block. Below this lies the central cruciform
complex of cattle and pig feeding houses with a covered
manure pit at the bottom. Accommodation for horses
and storage for equipment runs up the left side
of the site.

In the years of economic uncertainty following the removal of corn
price protection in 1846, arable farmers were advised to place greater
emphasis on livestock not only because it made them less heavily
reliant upon corn but also because the resulting manure would allow
yields to increase. For this to be effective, however, money had to be
pumped into the infrastructure of the farm – into land drainage, the
reorganisation of field patterns, laying new farm roads and construction of new buildings.

A common feature in the improvement of an agricultural estate at
this time was the erection of an entirely new range of buildings for the
home farm. These would usually incorporate many of the latest
design features and would be the subject of scrutiny by experts from
near and far; they were a public proclamation of the status of the
landowner, and his agent or bailiff, in the new world of scientific
agriculture. Amongst those that survive are numbered some great

The processing house at Coleshill with behind it the
stackyard at first floor level. This whole site is now
almost entirely redundant for modern agriculture.
The buildings have been restored by the owners,
the National Trust, and are used for administrative
and general storage purposes.

agricultural monuments which represent the highest attempts to
transform the dilapidated and ill-equipped farmstead of the past into
an efficient manufactory worthy of the industrial age. One example is
the home farm of the Earl of Radnor's Coleshill estate in Oxfordshire, where new buildings were designed by the agent and erected in
1852. In spite of problems caused when the building contractor failed
to complete the project as agreed,[7] the extensive facilities provided
on this large farm of 500 acres of arable and 300 acres of grass made it a
showpiece for the ideals of high farming.

In layout, the Coleshill farm reflects very well the state of the art at
mid-century. For the purposes of economising labour, the buildings
are arranged to follow the natural flow of materials. The logical
progression, therefore, was from the storage of corn and fodder crops
in the stackyard at the top to their conversion into feed and litter in a

Looking down through the main livestock building at
Coleshill from the processing house end. Pig fatting
boxes were located to the left and stalls for cattle to
the right. A tramway ran down this central passage
carrying tubs loaded with feed. Half-way along the
wall at the left can be seen one of the access holes
for feed into the box on the other side.

large processing house adjoining, and their distribution down
through the houses beyond for fattening livestock. This central core
was completed by the large covered storage pit for manure, beyond
which was a fattening house for sheep. The style of production was
deliberately that of the factory, with raw materials going in at one end
to emerge at the other as finished products in the form of high-
quality grain and meat for market and manure to be returned to the
fields. Around the periphery of the site were located those buildings
which, though still important, were not immediately involved in the
primary production line. They included the sheds and yards for
calving cows and lambing ewes, the stables for working horses and
storage areas for field implements.

Some additional features of the plan[8] continued the quest for
labour-saving efficiency. The whole steading, for example, was built

into a naturally sloping site so that the stackyard was at first-floor level relative to the processing house. Each stack could then be brought along and fed straight into the top of the threshing machine without the lifting that would normally be required. In the main fattening house, feed was distributed and manure collected with the help of a simple tramway laid along the central access passage. The gentle downward gradient of this building considerably lightened the work of pushing the laden tram tubs and so reduced the labour requirement.

Barns of the traditional form, cavernous inside and costly to maintain, were no longer a necessity. Instead, the real heart of these farms was the processing house with, in the case of Coleshill, the beat coming from the steady pulse of a steam engine. This supplied power to all the machinery within, the position of which was very precisely decided by the flow of the production process. The grain that emerged at the end of the threshing, winnowing and dressing sequence was stored on the first floor over an access way for wagons to facilitate dispatch. Straw, in addition to its use as litter, could take a different route to be chopped into chaff, mixed with sliced turnips and then steamed in chests before being loaded into the adjacent tramway tubs and served up as feed for the waiting cattle and pigs further down the slope. This treatment made the most of the nutritional potential of the straw and avoided the more costly alternative of hay. These operations were carried out on a regular basis week by week as needed, gradually consuming the reserves of material held in the stackyard and storage bins.

The thinking behind the Coleshill layout showed through in other prestigious farms around the country built at the same time. At Lymm in Cheshire, for example, was a farm designed by George Dean, the plans of which were published in 1850.[9] Dean was a land agent, agricultural engineer and architect, with commissions on the Leicester estate in Norfolk and the royal estate at Windsor to his credit. In his writings, he explained his work in great detail and proclaimed the virtues of scientific farming. He felt that too many farmsteads were being constructed by builders who knew little about farming and that consequently too much money was being spent on the wrong things, whereas 'there is no doubt that by exercising skill and care the expenditure on farm buildings may, in general, be diminished considerably; affording at the same time increased accom-

Lymm Farm, Cheshire, designed by G. A. Dean in the late 1840s. In the centre is the two-storey processing area with all machinery driven from a steam engine installed at the rear. On either side are cattle houses, connected by internal tramway to the feed stores. To the right is the corner of a large complex for calves, sheep and pigs, while at the far end runs a line of horse stables.

modation, combined with economy of labour'.[10] This was the most useful contribution that science could make to agriculture following the repeal of price protection, for the farmer now needed to produce more at lower cost.

For these reasons, Dean was happy to provide full specifications for farms of the approved kind. They went beyond details of layout to include optimum dimensions for the different categories of building involved and the recommended materials to use. Slates were light, durable, cheap and the preferred choice for roofs, while walls should be of brick or stone. The selection of timber, however, depended very much upon the purpose for which it was required. Straight Norwegian fir was suited to roof framing, larch was strong enough for posts, rails and floors, elm best for rafters or weatherboarding and

Farm at Charlton, near Ludwell in Dorset, designed by
G. A. Dean who published the plans in 1867. The view
here is to the south from the stackyard to the taller
processing house. A steam engine housed in the
building adjacent on the right powered the threshing
machine; the covered way was used as a straw store.

poplar, with its resistance to parasites, ideal for cheese rooms.
Typical of Dean's attention to detail was his advice that in the
stables, which were to be cool, well ventilated and drained, the
harness should be stored behind the horses in recesses fronted with
sliding doors so that the brasswork was protected from the ammoniacal atmosphere.

The Lymm farm embodied the principles Dean had outlined.
Overall, it was rectangular in form and followed what had become a
commonly accepted orientation of processing and storage areas on
the northern side, livestock yards on the warmer south, and the horse
and implement accommodation ranged down the other two sides.
The house occupied the south-western corner of the site, where the
need for both privacy and contact with the operations of the farm
could be satisfied. Although the plans of a Dean farm may appear
highly complex, in the flesh they are invariably revealed as being
much more straightforward and restrained. Certainly at both Lymm
and the Charlton Manor Farm, near Ludwell in Dorset,[11] the notice-

The same Dean farm at Charlton with the former steam
engine and boiler house in the distance on the left and
in the foreground a row of cart and wagon sheds surmounted
by granaries at the upper level. On the other side of this
block, to the right, was a layout of yards and shelter
sheds for cattle.

able lack of significant architectural embellishment suggests that
Dean meant what he said about excessive expenditure. Lymm was a
large farmstead intended originally to house 90 fatting cattle, up to
200 pigs and unspecified numbers of sheep, calves and cows, as well as
the usual complement of horses. The buildings are therefore extensive and yet, constructed as they are from local stone quarried on the
estate and set under slate roofs, their design was strictly functional.
In total the bill, including the house and all machinery and fittings
throughout was £2,900. Dean does not say how large the farm was but
judging from the extent of accommodation provided, the cost of the
buildings on an acreage ratio was reasonable by contemporary standards.

The real objective, of course, was to achieve the best possible
combination of economy with efficiency. For Dean, this meant
ensuring that these superficially rather ordinary buildings were very
well equipped technologically. So there were, for example, two
tramway systems operating laterally, one through the fat cattle

houses and processing area, the other through the middle of the piggeries, sheep houses and calf yards. Next to the central processing building was located a steam engine with a long list of quite separate functions in order to gain maximum benefit from the outlay entailed. In addition to threshing and dressing, the engine powered machines for grinding beans, bruising oats and cutting chaff. All feed was prepared on the first floor, from where it dropped, when required, into the trucks below for distribution down the lines of cattle-fattening boxes ranged on either side. Attached to the threshing machine was an elevator that raised the straw back up to the first floor and stored it throughout the loft space over the cattle until needed as litter in the boxes. Outside, on the northern edge of the site, unthatched stacks were kept under simple wooden sheds before being dropped onto trucks and hauled by steam winch into the processing area. Such a system may now seem rather bizarre but it was a logical extension of the agricultural manufactory theory, need not in itself involve great expense and, in Dean's opinion, would save 10 per cent on the labour cost of thatching, transporting and lifting stacks in the ordinary way.

Dean and his fellow practitioners were fully aware that the justific-ation of installations like these depended entirely upon the size of the farm. The larger it was, the greater the throughput of materials, the more fully occupied the fixed machinery would be and the stronger the potential of economising on labour costs. Strictly financial considerations, however, did not necessarily always apply on the landlord's home farm, where there was often greater freedom for the architect or engineer to indulge some of his more elaborate notions. Nor were they paramount on those farms owned and run by success-ful entrepreneurs from the world of industry and commerce, for whom agriculture was by no means the sole, or major, source of income. Nevertheless, economic realities were relevant to the great mass of ordinary tenanted farms around the country, a significant proportion of which were being modernised during this period. Here great care was needed to prevent the over-endowment of a small farm with facilities that would not yield a return. The right balance was not everywhere achieved but the cost factor, affecting as it did broader questions of design, materials and types of equipment, did emerge as the leading element in discussions on farm-building con-struction.

THE WORK OF J. BAILEY DENTON

Cost-effectiveness was indeed a primary concern of J. Bailey Denton in his magnificent *Farm Homesteads of England,* published in 1863. This work was related to Denton's position as engineer to the General Land Drainage and Improvement Company, which was one of the major institutions providing loans for the construction of new farm buildings. The book was intended to promote the principles of good design by illustrating thirty newly constructed farmsteads drawn from the work of different architects on different types of farm throughout the country. It is, therefore, a textbook of best practice springing once again from the uncomplimentary parallels being drawn between agriculture and industry:

'to farm successfully with defective and ill-arranged buildings is no more practicable than to manufacture profitably in scattered, inconvenient workshops in place of one harmoniously contrived, completely fitted mill.'[12]

In his own very full recommendations about the siting, layout and construction of buildings, Denton suggested a sliding scale of expenditure related to farm size. The outlay on farmstead and house combined should, he believed, range from £4 10s per acre for farms of 1,000 acres and over, to £6 per acre for those of 500–1,000 acres and about £7 per acre for the smaller farms down to 200 acres. So at the top of the range the very largest mixed farms could be equipped with an extensive steading costing perhaps £5,000 while the smaller holdings, lacking the economies of scale, would have to make do with much less.

Denton gives a very good illustration of how advanced design theory could be applied, in an economical way, to the needs of a small farm. Lower Toothill Farm, on Viscount Palmerston's Broadlands estate in Hampshire, was equipped in 1861 with a new set of buildings designed by Denton himself and similar in form to those of his own Chisfield Manor Farm near Stevenage. At £1,715 the cost, for a 200-acre farm, was rather more than that suggested in his own recommendations, especially as the price of the house was not included. The figure had been inflated, however, by a heavier than normal

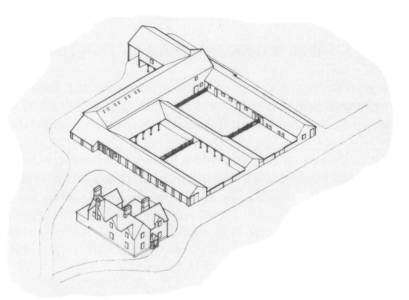

Toothill Farm, Hampshire, drawn from an illustration in
J. Bailey Denton's *Farm Homesteads of England*, 1863. The
horse gearing was housed in the building at the top of the
site where it drove the equipment in the adjoining processing
house. Next to this came the barn and wagon shed with
granary above. Accommodation for livestock was arranged
in the two outer wings.

outlay on foundations due to the sloping nature of the site. It was a
simple no-frills layout with a stackyard giving onto a storage and
processing block, more like a conventional barn in this case, ranged
across the north side. To the south of this were four open yards, three
for young cattle and one for pigs, each of which was equipped with an
open-fronted shelter and feeding area. Attached to the feed-processing section, and flanking the yards on the eastern side, was a line of
buildings with accommodation for eight fatting cattle, for six cows
and a number of pigs. On the opposite side, a similar line adjacent to
the implement and wagon sheds held the stables for working and
riding horses.

This farm was too small to merit the installation of either a steam
engine or a threshing machine. Power was instead provided by a horse
gear housed to the rear of the processing building, where the necessary chaff-cutting, root-slicing and cake-breaking machinery was
positioned on an intermediate floor. Threshing was done in the

traditional way by hand on a specially prepared floor located inside the large double doors of the barn. It was not the sophistication but the effectiveness of the design that mattered and this meant attention to detail. For example, all the buildings were well guttered, so that not only was a considerable quantity of rainwater kept out of the yards, where it would have diluted and spoilt the manure, but this water could be led away to an underground tank and used, through the aid of a pump, to supply all the drinking troughs around the site as required. Farmsteads like Toothill demonstrated that a well arranged, self-contained unit providing for all the needs of the farm could be supplied at reasonable cost.

THE FINANCING OF IMPROVEMENTS

On most estates, the cost of providing new buildings on the tenanted farms was met by the landowner, although the tenant was often expected to arrange for the cartage of materials at his own expense. This provoked the common criticism that disruption was caused through the removal of horses from farm operations when they could least be spared. In the case of Toothill Farm, the estate had borrowed the money for the new buildings from the General Land Drainage and Improvement Company, founded in 1849, with which Denton was connected. It was one of a number of organisations established in the wake of the repeal of the Corn Laws for the purpose of advancing loans to finance farm improvements that would ease the transfer to free trade conditions. The Government had started things off by making available a sum of £2 million to assist with field drainage. So popular was the scheme that subsequently private improvement companies emerged to satisfy the demand for loans and also extend the coverage by including other eligible works, among them buildings. It has been estimated that something like £14 million in all was borrowed between 1846 and 1882 and a quarter of this was spent on the construction of new farm buildings.[13] No account is taken here of the improvements paid for out of the landowner's own reserves rather than by loans. In some areas, particularly where the agricultural income of the estate was supplemented by industrial or commercial interests, the programme of work was very considerable.

The links between the landed classes and commerce could be very close and the Duke of Bedford is a prime example of a landowner using non-agricultural income to assist with the funding of improvements to the rural estate. The Duke's various interests included the ownership of 119 acres of prime land in central London and also of the site near Tavistock beneath which Devon Great Consols operated one of the biggest copper mines in the world. This was the kind of backing that allowed the seventh Duke to spend over a quarter of a million pounds on developing the Bedfordshire estate, and over £100,000 on his Thorney estate in Cambridgeshire, between 1842 and his death in 1861.[14] Farm buildings absorbed a significant proportion of these amounts.

At Thorney, where large sums had already been spent on draining wet fenland and claiming it for advanced agriculture, the need now was for suitably equipped farmsteads that would enable the tenants to gain the most from the rich, fertile soil. Two farms close to Thorney itself show the style of building that was adopted by the estate and adjusted to match the size of holding. Old Hall Farm was built in 1861 at a cost of £1,500 and designed by the agent, Robert Mein, for an area of 300 acres, 250 of which were arable. St Vincent's Cross Farm was contemporary, but almost twice the size, so accordingly the buildings, including some nearby cottages, were that much more expensive at £3,500. On both farmsteads the characteristic feature was a range of processing and ancillary buildings, such as granary and wagon shed, along the northern side, with a series of small open yards flanked by shelter sheds to the south. The one dealt with the heavy yields of grain and fodder crops while the other provided a convenient method of converting the large quantities of straw produced into good-quality manure. A limited amount of fattening accommodation, boxes or stalls, was incorporated into the plan for the final preparation of cattle for market. At St Vincent's Cross, the two-storey processing building was equipped with steam-powered machinery and there was space in the yards to overwinter 76 cattle. The smaller Old Hall Farm was entirely single-storey with no steam engine or threshing machine and yard capacity was reduced to 40 beasts. Both farmsteads were constructed from bricks made on the estate and roofed with Welsh slates.

Amongst other agricultural estates of the front rank, there were some similarly comprehensive schemes of improvement at this time. At Holkham in Norfolk, the continuous programme of work over many years affected to some degree all seventy of the estate's holdings and included a commission for Dean to design an extensive new steading for the 1,200-acre Egmere Farm.[15] On the Earl of Pembroke's Wilton estate in Wiltshire the standard of building on the tenanted farms was widely praised by the procession of agriculturists who went to see and admire. In the late 1850s, for example, the existing buildings at Netherhampton Farm were cleared and replaced with a planned layout principally involving a combination of both open and covered yards running south from a long lateral processing block. For such well constructed and equipped accommodation the price was of course high, in this case £5,000 for a farm of under 600 acres. In theory, the landowner would be aiming to recoup with interest this kind of expenditure by charging the tenant a higher rent. While in the special circumstances of the Thorney estate the Duke of Bedford achieved an 8 per cent return on his outlay,[16] for many other estates the figure was more likely to be in the region of from 2 to $2\frac{1}{2}$ per cent, or roughly half what might have been expected if the same money had been invested commercially. The landlord was dependent upon the tenant's ability to pay and this in turn was directly linked to the current prosperity or otherwise of farming itself.

Nevertheless, when it came to improvements there were other considerations in addition to the purely financial. The hereditary estate was the cornerstone of a family's position in society and, for the sake of permanency, required to be handed on to the succeeding generation in a satisfactory state of repair. For some, inherited debts and legal entanglements made this an impossibility but there were many landowners who took the stewardship of their estates very seriously and were prepared to invest money in improvement works of a lasting kind. To this end, it was in the interests of the landlord to see to it that his estate was farmed in a professional and responsible manner. Accordingly, he needed to attract as tenants men of the necessary calibre and capital who would farm profitably and maintain the land in good heart. One of the theories of the day was that by providing first-class buildings, a first-class tenant would be installed on the farm and, equally important, stay there.

When times were bad in the last quarter of the century, new buildings were often a bargaining counter, supplied in an attempt to bolster the ailing tenant and encourage him to hang on as best he could. Nothing could be worse than a vacant farm going to ruin, so

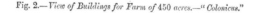

Fig. 2.—*View of Buildings for Farm of 450 acres.—" Colonicus."*

Farm plan by Richard Waite of Duffield that received a
commendation in the competition held in association with
the London International Exhibition of 1879. The steading
is entirely covered, with the two main cattle yards
divided by a central group of fatting stalls. To the south
is the farmhouse, and to the north the processing building
served by a stackyard tramway. From the *JRASE*, 1879.

the money spent on improvements, perhaps without hope of adequate return, was the price to be paid. In most cases the work
involved constructing additional accommodation for livestock at the
farmstead itself, accompanied by extra facilities for the preparation
of feed. More than ever, economy was now the order of the day and
the discussion was rather more about adaptation of existing buildings
than complete renewal. In his book published in 1891, the land agent
Dudley Clarke devoted a whole chapter to the 'Remodelling of Old
Homesteads'. This would have been unthinkable in the texts of
thirty years earlier. He acknowledges that the sad plight of farming
had made it impossible for many landowners to make the expenditure
that was now necessary on buildings, but

'even in these cases a good deal of improvement may be frequently
effected at a moderate outlay in many ways, by the adaptation of old

Inside the food mixing room on the ground floor of the
processing house at Common Farm. The steam engine was
sited here and the stairs at the far end led to granaries
and a chaff cutting room.

barns to more serviceable uses, the use of corrugated iron roofing
where suitable, and the judicious use of such materials as can be
procured on the estate, which, although perhaps of not very lasting
quality, may serve until the advent of better times.'[17]

It was also necessary to try to anticipate any likely future changes
in farming practice by incorporating as much flexibility as possible
into the arrangements. Bailey Denton had made the same point but
now, in the 1890s, it was put with much greater emphasis.

It was not, however, a case of make do and mend everywhere.
There are a good number of farmsteads dotted around the countryside that underwent complete transformation in the 1880s and 1890s.
One such is the Common Farm, at Watnall in Nottinghamshire, a
155-acre mostly arable farm which formed part of Earl Cowper's
estate and was supplied with a new steading in the mid-1880s. The

Feeding passage running through the covered accommodation
at Bexwell Hall Farm, Norfolk.

cost of construction was reckoned by the agent to be under £5 per acre, which, given the small size of the farm, was some way below the figures recommended by Denton in 1863. This was in line with the cost-consciousness of the times, for John Scott in his farm buildings book of 1890 quoted the same figures but said that, 'under the present circumstances of agriculture, no land will support that outlay on buildings'.[18]

Certainly there were few frills in the design at Watnall. The processing house, whilst well provided with steam-driven equipment, was unpretentious in scale and lacked the complexity and sophistication so characteristic of earlier years. Prime emphasis was given to the economical housing of stock, using open sheds and yards for the younger animals, and the conservation of manure in a covered pit. A similar formula can be seen on the 388-acre Bexwell Hall Farm, near Downham Market in Norfolk, where the buildings are of the same date. Here three lines of open yards for stock were separated by accompanying shelter sheds and areas of enclosed accommodation for cows, pigs and fatting cattle. In all, 10 calves and 60 or so pigs were bred and 25 fat cattle prepared for market during the course of the year. Passageways provided the connecting link between this housing and the main feed-preparation area running along the top of the site, which bore no special embellishment and, indeed, incorporated a much older converted barn. The principles that had so inspired the designs of mid-century were still present in the underlying logic of these layouts. The difference was that the confident assertion of mastery over the forces of agriculture had been replaced by the more sober stamp of pragmatism and caution.

2
The Victorian Farm
at Work

The capacity to harness appropriate technology was a prominent feature of the progressive Victorian farmstead and a decisive influence upon the layout of the central hub where the processing functions were carried out. A variety of power sources were available and the question of which was best in terms of performance and economy was one of the meatier areas of debate. Least preferred was wind power because of its innate unreliability and, at times, uncontrollability. The advantages of an apparently free form of energy were more than offset by the high cost of constructing and maintaining a windmill and by the need for a back-up means of power for when the wind failed. Earlier in the century, a few farmsteads, notably in Scotland and the English borders, were built with windmills in the stackyard to drive threshing and processing machinery. This became a much rarer practice during the Victorian period.

HORSE POWER

The most widely available power came from the horse. Rotary motion for a fixed threshing machine could be obtained through a gearing mechanism that was turned by horses walking in a circular path. The characteristic polygonal outhouses that once contained these horse 'gins' may still be seen today on farms, particularly in the Scottish border region, where mechanised threshing was first adopted on an extensive scale. The gin house at Old Hall Farm, Whittonstall in Northumberland, with its stone walls and slate roof was entirely typical of many constructed in the first half of the century. These substantial fixtures were not so common in the southern portion of the country, where mechanised threshing was slower to develop and where, by the early years of the reign, smaller, portable

Nineteenth-century round house at Old Hall Farm,
Whittonstall in Northumberland. This contained the
horse-powered drive mechanism to operate a threshing
machine in the adjacent barn.

horse-powered threshing units were gaining favour.

The horse was not particularly well suited to the labour of driving a
threshing machine. For one thing it was expensive: the number of
horses required varied between four and eight, occasionally going up
to ten, depending upon the size of the machine. In addition, they
would need a man and perhaps also a boy, during the day for general
supervision. All of this represented cost and diverted horse power
away from equally important seasonal work in the fields. There could
be a physical price to pay as well, for not only was the task of driving
the machine over long periods an exhausting one for the horses but
also the machine itself was prone to a jerkiness of motion, especially
when badly operated, that was transmitted back through the gearing.
Continuing improvements in design helped to eradicate the worst
effects of this but even so the stress upon the limbs and muscles of the
horses was significant.[1]

The result of all this was that during the second half of the century
horse power was more commonly used to drive the smaller machines
such as chaff cutters, root slicers and cake breakers. Although light

and easily portable arrangements of horse gearing became increasingly popular, the older fixed variety with big overhead spur-wheel was still available. For example, it was the principal power source at Toothill Farm, Hampshire, for the preparation of animal feed, while the threshing continued to be done by hand. Similarly on Bartletts Farm in Arborfield, Berkshire, a fixed two-horse gear, made by the London-based firm of Wedlake and dating from the 1860s, drove via line shafting the standard range of light equipment in the adjacent much older barn. These systems were cheap to acquire and would impose little in the way of extra load upon the farm's existing team of horses. Manor Farm, at Catterick in Yorkshire, was provided with a portable steam engine in the 1870s for the purposes of driving all the fixed equipment, including a threshing machine. The earlier six-horse gear was retained, however, to carry out occasional light work of the cutting and pulping variety when the engine was idle. It is likely that this was not a rare occurrence.

WATER POWER

Of far greater economy, assuming that it was available in sufficient strength, was water power. It was not unusual for fixed threshing machines erected on farms in England in the first half of the century to be driven by a waterwheel. The technology of water power had reached an advanced stage by this date and its applicability was amply demonstrated throughout the world of manufacturing industry. Viability in agriculture depended to a large degree on local factors for the water source could not necessarily be linked with the most appropriate setting for the farmstead. This was not, however, an insurmountable problem. By 1842, James Cunningham had supervised the installation of seventeen waterwheels on farms in the Scottish border country.[2] In a few cases, they could only be set up at a lower level, some distance away from the farm buildings, and were connected by lines of shafting. Although one example took 70 yards of shafting, at a rate of 8s per yard, to raise the power a height of 60ft, Cunningham nevertheless believed that in terms of cost this was preferable to a steam engine.

On substantial home farms and some of the larger tenanted holdings it might be financially possible to divert water courses, sometimes over long distances, in order to turn a wheel at the farmstead. Work of this kind could, exceptionally, be incorporated within an overall strategy of land or estate improvement. An early example of this was the programme carried out on the English estates of the Marquis of Stafford under the supervision of his very accomplished agent, James Loch.[3] Large sums were spent in the first two decades of the century on buildings and the reorganisation of farmland, in the course of which many of the farms were equipped with water-powered threshing machines. At one, Honnington Grange, on the Lilleshall estate in Shropshire, 36 acres of water meadow were created so that the supply for the machinery subsequently also irrigated the land. When the farm was further modernised in mid-century, feed-preparation machinery in the livestock building was driven from the waterwheel by means of a communicating line shaft that passed under the road. At a later date still, the wheel itself was replaced by a water turbine.

Through skilful engineering, the requirements of both land drainage and water power could be made to coincide. In Staffordshire, a district well known for its agricultural improvement in the early Victorian period, the Teddesley Hay estate of Lord Hatherton offered an example. Here the water collected from field drains was directed into a small man-made reservoir, from where it was led through an underground culvert for a distance of half a mile to a waterwheel in the farmstead. Thereafter, the water again disappeared beneath the surface and was used to irrigate water meadows elsewhere on the farm.[4] In the same county, an underground leat, over a mile long, brought water to the wheel at Coley Farm, Gnossal, dated 1842. Set within the central processing block, the breast-shot waterwheel, 20ft in diameter, was connected via shafting to three pairs of stones in the mill on one side and to threshing, dressing and chaff-cutting equipment arranged on the other. Furthermore, an elevator for lifting barley up to the storage floor in the adjacent malt house was also linked through a subsidiary length of shafting. Not all of this equipment could be, or indeed needed to be, powered simultaneously, so simple clutch devices operated on the pulley wheels to throw out of gear those items not being used at any one time.

Notable amongst the farmstead waterwheels that survive in England is the one on the Tew estate in Oxfordshire. J. C. Loudon, well known through his later prolific writings on rural management,

leased part of the estate for three years from 1808, during the course
of which he had built at Tew Lodge a new arrangement of farm
buildings owing much to contemporary practice in his native Scotland. An overshot waterwheel, installed by an Edinburgh millwright
in 1809, drove a threshing machine as well as bruising, bean-breaking
and straw-cutting equipment in a processing house that required
seven or eight men for full operation. The farmstead was of very light
construction and short duration so that all that now remains at the
site is the brickwork forming the original wheelpit.[5] It is likely,
however, that it influenced the subsequent incorporation of a waterwheel into the layout at nearby Traceys Farm. Here the backshot
wheel, 16ft in diameter, was set adjacent to the barn or processing
house but below ground level, and received water from an underground leat. Iron teeth on the rim of the wheel turned a vertical
wooden shaft that took the drive up and into the building. This
installation was in service throughout the Victorian period.

STEAM POWER

Notwithstanding the range of alternatives, by mid-century it was the
steam engine that was in vogue and commanding most attention.
Steam-driven threshing machines had been around for some time:
Trevithick's engine of 1812 for use on a Cornish farm is preserved in
the London Science Museum, and by the 1820s there were a number
of large, heavy beam-engines at work in Scotland and the English
borders. Although able to perform the work of threshing quite well,
these low-pressure condensing engines were expensive to purchase
and not noted for their fuel economy. They did not therefore readily
commend themselves to farmers elsewhere in the country – away
from the coal-mining areas – where fuel was dear and human labour
cheap. For the farm tenant there was the added question of whether
he would receive adequate recompense for his outlay on the installation of a fixed engine when his term expired.

Continuing improvements to the technology served to remove at
least some of these objections during the early years of Victoria's
reign. Various configurations of compact, non-condensing, direct-
acting engines emerged, which avoided the use of a cumbersome
beam and utilised higher pressures and the expansive qualities of

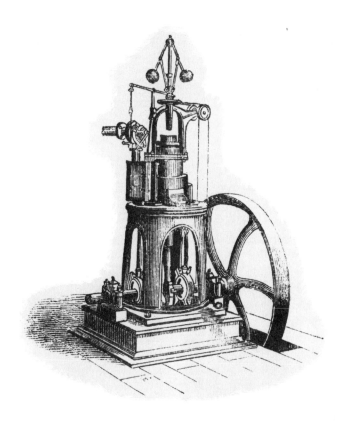

A table steam engine suitable for farm use. From the 1851
catalogue of Ransomes & May of Ipswich.

steam to operate more economically. One such was the table engine,
with a vertical cylinder set upon a raised platform over the crankshaft.
The 1851 catalogue of Ransomes & May of Ipswich featured a table
engine of 4 horsepower and praised its sturdiness, its reliability and
the ease of fixing it within a building, which required only the
minimum of floor support and no attachment to the walls. It was,
claimed the manufacturers, 'peculiarly adapted' to the driving of
threshing and processing machinery and could without difficulty be
introduced into an already existing arrangement where hitherto the
power had been provided by horse gear.

The crank of a steam engine could also be positioned above rather

Engine house at Walls Court Farm near Bristol. The engine
was of the vertical type and the surviving flywheel, with
crank just to the left, is shown here. The main drive
shaft passed through the wall and distributed power
throughout the processing house by means of connecting
line shafts and belt pulleys.

than below the cylinder, although the shaft and flywheel would then
normally need to be supported by a wall bearing. Engines of this type
receive frequent mention in the mid-century agricultural literature
and it is likely that the one installed in Walls Court Farm, on the
estate of the Duke of Beaufort near Bristol, employed the overhead
crank design. The farmstead was constructed in 1855 to the plans of
George Godwin, who was both an architect and editor of *The*

Builder. It served a holding of 645 acres, over three-quarters of it laid to grass, which had undergone extensive improvement, thorough drainage included, during the tenancy of Thomas Proctor, a wealthy Bristol manufacturer of artificial manures who had taken up farming.[6] The buildings were an impressive showpiece for the new farming, with first-class arrangements for dairying, and the breeding and feeding of Shorthorns, organised in three lines of sheds linked by tramway. Covered accommodation was provided for 135 cattle and 8 working horses out of a total livestock complement that included a flock of over 600 Southdown sheep. Amongst the enlightened extras was a schoolroom incorporated into the complex for the education of the labourers' children. Facilities for the housing of implements and wagons, as well as more horses, were situated in the adjacent 84-acre Stanley Farm, which was run as a combined unit with Walls Court by Mr Proctor. In recent years, the main farmstead has been encroached upon by industrial development and henceforward will be a centre for leisure rather than agricultural activity.

The Walls Court steam engine was connected via shafting and drive belts to the feed-processing machines located at first-floor level. Beneath them were steaming chambers, supplied from the engine boiler, where musty or low-grade hay could be treated, sometimes with straw added as well, to convert it into something that cattle would be prepared to eat. This supplementary use of steam was often practised where engines were installed. At the other end of the country, for example, was the Northumbrian farm of High House, Matfen, a remote 364-acre mixed holding, just north of Hadrian's Wall, where the Angus family were tenants throughout the first fifty years of Victoria's reign. Improvements and additions had been made to the farmstead at intervals over a long period and, as with many other farms of the region, steam power had been introduced in the second half of the century. Here roots and chaff could be steamed in chests while the engine itself drove the cake breaker, chaff cutter and other machinery.

During the 1850s, the horizontal steam engine, with cylinder and crankshaft bolted to a cast-iron bedplate, came to the fore. It employed the minimum of moving parts, was easy to maintain and was adaptable to all kinds of uses. Ransomes & Sims developed a successful version, winner of many prizes at agricultural shows, that was available in sizes from 4 to 12 nominal horsepower at a cost with

Chaff cutter on the first floor of the Walls Court processing
house. Above on the right is the shafting that originally
conveyed the drive from the steam engine to
individual machines.

boiler of from £150 to £270. Another major manufacturer was the
Lincoln firm of Clayton & Shuttleworth and it was a 10 horsepower
example of theirs that was chosen as the power base for Chalkpits
Farm, on the Englefield estate in Berkshire, when it was built in
1856.[7] This, the home farm on an estate that also went to considerable lengths to improve the quality of buildings on its tenanted farms,
ran to 546 acres, half of which were arable while the rest supported a
herd of 200 Shorthorn cattle and a flock of 600 sheep.

In layout and construction the farmstead was well planned and
functional rather than spectacular. Following the conventional
north–south orientation, the block housing machinery was positioned between the stackyard, with its row of six timber-framed
Dutch barns, and the livestock areas, which comprised a fattening
house, piggery, dairy unit, yard for young stock and stables. All the
machines for threshing, chaff cutting, cake crushing, grinding and

Feed processing room at Home Farm, Berkeley Castle in
Gloucestershire. Situated on the first floor next to the
granaries, it was powered by steam. The line shaft,
protected by wooden casing, runs along the back
of the room with a small pulley to drive the
grain bruising mill in the centre while the
larger pulley wheel behind takes the power
to other machinery.

corn bruising that were driven by steam were located on the first floor.
The engine was reckoned to consume about 8 cwt of coal a day but
such was its capacity, cutting 5 tons of chaff per day for example, that
it was only required to work for three days in a week. It survives
today, in working order, at the equally well equipped estate yard close
by that dates from the same period.

Although not the case at Englefield, it was not unusual for a home
farm and estate workshops to occupy buildings that were contiguous.
Coleshill is one example and the home farm at Westonbirt,
Gloucestershire, built in the mid-1850s, is another.[8] Here the steam
engine installation was placed so as to drive the agricultural
machinery in the farm on one side and the equipment in the sawmill
on the other. A similar practice was adopted on the Marquis of Bath's

The horizontal, single cylinder steam engine by
Clayton & Shuttleworth of Lincoln that was
installed in 1856 at Chalkpits Farm,
Englefield in Berkshire.

The home farm at Westonbirt in Gloucestershire dating from
the middle of the century. Immediately to the left of the
archway was the threshing and processing complex powered
by a steam engine located to the right. This also drove
a sawmill and other machinery in the estate yard further
over and adjacent to the farm.

The home farm for the Longleat estate in Wiltshire, from
Copland's *Agriculture Ancient & Modern*, 1866. Beyond the
chimney is the estate yard with its steam-driven sawmill.
Below is the farm with the processing house, linked
through a covered way to the main livestock accommodation
area distinguished by its large central covered yard. The
house at the top left is for the farm bailiff and that to the
right for the clerk of works in the yard.

home farm at Longleat when it was built to the designs of the Oxford
architect William Wilkinson in 1860.[9] The farm and estate yard were
sited back to back with a 16 horsepower Clayton & Shuttleworth
horizontal engine between them, so that full advantage could be
taken of the versatility of steam. In the mill it was connected to a large
grindstone and four saws, among them a circular saw and rack bench
for cutting felled timber from the estate and another for converting
waste pieces into small blocks for use as fuel in the boiler. Above the
boilerhouse was a steam-heated drying-room for boards and joinery,
while next door on the farm side were bins for steaming chaff as well
as the complete range of processing equipment.

By these means the steam engine was kept more fully occupied, thereby justifying the expense, than if restricted to farming operations alone. On the more conventional farm, the superior power of the steam engine could be satisfactorily demonstrated through a potential daily threshing output of 50 quarters, or 400 bushels, as opposed to the 30 quarters that was the upper limit when using four or six horses. A whole stack could be dealt with in a matter of hours and the farmer was able to dispatch his grain to market without delay whenever the price was favourable. The problem, however, was that there were not enough additional tasks for a fixed engine to do in order to earn its keep for the rest of the year, so, while the northern border counties and the Lothians of Scotland, for example, were enthusiastic owing to the special factors operating there, England for the most part needed more convincing.

PORTABLE ENGINES

Many of the doubts were answered by the portable steam engine, which was steadily improving throughout the 1850s and 1860s and which could either be hired to perform specific operations such as threshing or be purchased to cover a range of work not necessarily entirely based on the farmstead. The early portables of the 1840s had suffered too much from excessive vibration, bad maintenance and poor fuel economy to challenge the supremacy of the stationary engine. The commonly held view was that

'a fixed engine will be steadier in its action, more effective in power for its size, and more durable than a portable one, and therefore always to be preferred whenever its use is required in one and the same place.'[10]

Now all this was changing. With the growing recognition, even on the larger farms, of the greater flexibility provided by movable engines and threshing machines, some of the mid-century theory of the planned farmstead, radiating outwards from a central power base, began to crumble.

Even so, the days of the stationary steam engine were not over yet. Indeed, it enjoyed something of a revival in the last quarter of the century when, following the renewed emphasis on livestock farming,

Home farm, Longleat. The estate yard is in the foreground with the sawmill and woodworking shops located within the arched central structure. Everything to the left of it is agricultural.

the new small high-pressure vertical engine was often employed to drive simple machines for preparing cattle feed. Going back to the Englefield estate in Berkshire, for example, not only were many of the farms fitted with covered cattle yards in the early 1880s but also engines were installed to drive the chaff cutters, cake mills, oat crushers and root pulpers. Ufton Green Farm, to take one of many, was supplied in April 1882 with a Robey 5 horsepower vertical engine and boiler combined at a cost of £112. The installation work was carried out by the estate, with the landlord paying for some of the fittings, while the tenant made the outlay on the machinery.[11] Similar engines also proved useful in the dairy, where the steam could be used for room heating and for sterilising equipment as well as for providing power. By the end of the century, the incoming internal combustion engine, in its small, versatile stationary form, was being taken up in increasing numbers for the multitude of miscellaneous tasks around the farm.

TRAMWAYS

Threshing remained the paramount agricultural processing operation but through the agency of the travelling steam engine, whether
portable or self-propelled, it had been liberated from the farmstead
itself. Now the machinery could be set up wherever it was most
convenient to build the stacks. This effectively removed the earlier
logistical problem, which had exercised so many minds, of how to
convey the stacks to a central, fixed threshing machine with the
minimum of time and trouble. In particular, it halted further
development of the stackyard tramway, which had been of such
apparent potential in the 1850s. As it was, a number of different
systems were devised. One, tried out on Lord Bateman's Uphampton
Farm in Herefordshire, had a line running through an annexe of the
processing house, adjacent to the threshing machine, and emerging
on either side to split into three branches. The trucks on which
the cornstacks were built thus ran by gravity from one side of the
stackyard into the threshing area to be unloaded and then out on
the other, where they were stored. To counter any claims of extra-
vagance, the tramway itself was described as being cheap and the
trucks as being constructed of rough wood mounted on old railway
axles.[12]

The other stackyard systems preferred parallel branch tramways
bisected by an arterial line that ran straight into the processing
building. This left the question of how to transfer the trucks from
one to the other. J.C. Morton described one solution – a sunken
main line with a carriage onto which trucks could be run from the
branch lines running at right angles.[13] Other versions kept the single
level and relied on turntables at each interchange; G.H. Andrews
designed a special truck with two sets of wheels, at 90° to each other,
either of which could be brought into play by means of a lever.[14]

No surviving examples of stackyard lines are known. They affected
only a small proportion of farms, were overtaken by events and, by
virtue of being barely beyond the experimental stage, were doubtless
to a lesser or greater extent defective as well. Some farms that were
originally equipped in this way can, however, be identified. Sancton
Hill Farm, near Market Weighton, Humberside, was built in the
early 1860s to the designs of its owner, John Wells, a farmer and land

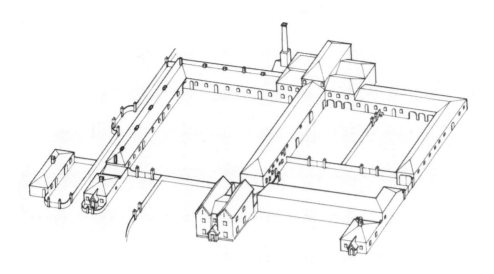

Sancton Hill Farm, near Market Weighton in Humberside,
built in the early 1860s. On the north side is the steam
threshing unit, served by a stackyard tramway at the rear,
with open yards flanked by stock houses to the south.
From a drawing in J. Bailey Denton's *Farm Homesteads
of England,* 1863.

agent. The new farmstead, built of locally made brick, occupied a
central site on the 350-acre holding and replaced earlier buildings that
were located down in the village. With the stackyard on the north
side occupying a higher part of the sloping ground, the tramway was
able to deliver the crop directly onto the first floor of the processing
building and into the waiting threshing machine, which was driven by
a well appointed fixed steam engine. The rest of the layout was rather
dislocated in its arrangement, although individual components, such
as the implement yard and the cattle sheds, were of a high order.

Eastwood Manor Farm in Somerset is another splendidly Victorian creation that included a stackyard tramway amongst its
features. Here William Taylor, a former butler who had married well
and become a rich man, built in 1850 a new farmstead for the 970-acre
estate. A man in his position could afford to be indulgent, so not only
were all the technology and the design of the latest kind but the whole

Eastwood Manor Farm, Somerset, with its two covered yards
flanked by buildings for the accommodation of livestock.
At the rear was a water-powered processing complex
served by a stackyard tramway.

building possessed in its symmetry an air of stylish grace. No
subsequent occupants have managed to dispel this impression, and
the family of the present owners have used and protected the
buildings with great sympathy for most of this century. The tramway
conveyed the stacks into the rear of the building, where all the
machinery, driven from an overshot waterwheel 27ft in diameter, was
located. Water was a convenient source of power in the neighbourhood and in this case was collected in ponds above the farm, led onto
the wheel and then piped away underground to be used for irrigation
purposes further down. One rare item of contemporary machinery
survives on the first floor of the farmstead – a chaff cutter, by Robert
Maynard of the Whittlesford Works near Cambridge, driven through
belting from the line shafting below. The fixed threshing machine has
gone but in its place a Clayton & Shuttleworth portable machine
dating from the early years of this century and now powered by
electricity, is still used to produce a clean sample of grain.

THE HOUSING OF STOCK

Changing attitudes towards the housing of stock, especially cattle, were also embodied at Eastwood. In the first place, this was an entirely covered farmstead with the two cattle yards roofed in corrugated iron. Agricultural use of this material on such a scale was still a novelty at mid-century and became much more common over the following thirty years. While its capacity to provide light, low-cost roofing was fully recognised, doubts about its durability restricted take-up in the early years until the need for economy became the predominant factor (the question of how to halt further deterioration of the non-standard and now irreplaceable corrugated iron poses one of the biggest conservation problems at Eastwood today). The arguments for and against open and covered yards led to a lively debate in the 1850s and 1860s. In the covered yard the manure was not subject to dilution by rainwater, smaller quantities of straw were required and the stock, protected from the elements, required less food to maintain a given body weight. On the other hand, the cost of roofing had to be taken into account, large arable farms – especially on the eastern side of the country – had an excess of straw to be disposed of, and some exposure to the weather was reckoned to produce healthier and hardier animals. As a result, an intermediate stage was also popular, in which, as on the Duke of Bedford's Thorney estate, small open yards were accompanied by open-fronted shelter sheds. Later in the century the pendulum swung more decisively in favour of the covered yard and it was not uncommon for a very basic form of roofing structure to be thrown over existing open areas. Of the farms previously mentioned, Netherhampton in Wiltshire, Honnington Grange in Shropshire and Manor House, Catterick, in Yorkshire, can all provide instances where this occurred.

In addition to the yards, facilities for the more intensive feeding of stock were usually a standard feature on the larger holdings during the high farming decades. Here, the cattle could be put through a batch process of final fattening and preparation for market, while at the same time converting rich fodder into high-quality manure. Opinion differed as to the most effective means of achieving both objectives within the bounds of economic good sense. Discussion centred principally upon the respective merits of stall and box

Tramway running down the feeding passage at the back of
cattle stalls in Honnington Grange Farm, Shropshire.
From here there was easy access through the openings
on the left to the feed troughs and above for hay into
the racks. A water supply pipe runs along the top
of the low wall.

feeding, measuring the lower first cost of the one against the apparent
qualitative gains of the other. The space occupied by each beast in a
stall was about 40 square feet, as opposed to the 90 square feet or
more when boxes were used, which accounts for the difference in
construction costs. Against this, the greater freedom of movement
permitted in a box was said to induce a calmer disposition so that less
nervous energy was expended and more weight gained from the same
quantity of feed. Moreover, none of the accumulating manure was
allowed to run to waste and it grew in quality from the thorough
trampling that it received under hoof. It is not difficult to find farms
where one of these systems was adopted while a number opted for
maximum flexibility and used both.

A typical stall arrangement comprised double compartments,
about 8ft wide and separated by wooden divisions, where a pair of
beasts were tied by the neck. At their heads were feed and water

troughs, often surmounted by a hay rack. Easy access to these was gained from the feeding passage on the other side, which in turn was in direct communication with the processing and preparation areas. It was along here that a simple tramway might justifiably be laid, as at Honnington Grange in Shropshire, to carry the wooden tubs that assisted with the distribution of feed. In a well organised plan, the water troughs were self-filling from the farm's own supply. All the rainwater that was so carefully guttered, to keep it out of the yards, was piped away to underground tanks from where it could be pumped when required, by whatever power source was installed, to a large cistern occupying an elevated position in the buildings and linked to all the troughs. With these means a farm could, in normal circumstances, benefit from a secure water supply all the year round. There was more pipework at the back of the stall for the floor sloped down slightly to a shallow gutter that collected the liquid elements of the waste. This was then led off to another underground tank for storage until pumped out for re-use. The dung was removed daily from the stalls and deposited in adjacent cattle yards, where it mingled with the straw litter and was absorbed into the manure-making process. In some cases, this clearance work was lightened by a second tramline running along the rear of the stalls.

The standard fattening box, by contrast, was a pen 9 or 10 ft square with a floor excavated between 1 and 2 ft below ground level. During each fattening cycle of about three months, it would hold a single untethered beast, which was fed, watered and supplied with frequent and liberal quantities of straw litter from the access passage running alongside. As the floor level of the box gradually rose from the build-up of manure, the troughs were moved up on adjustable brackets. At Englefield in Berkshire, the home farm was fitted with forty-two fattening boxes arranged in rows wide enough to allow cart access between them for periodic removal of the manure. Coleshill home farm in Oxfordshire still retains much of the internal timber structure of its boxes, including some larger double versions, although the farmstead itself is now redundant for agricultural purposes. Here the tramway in the feeding passage also served to convey manure into a covered pit sited at the lower end of the accommodation areas. Considerable care was taken to promote the well-being of stock in buildings such as these. Open ridge tiles or louvre-box ventilators on the roof, for example, supplied the

Double row of fattening pens or boxes at Coleshill Farm, Oxfordshire. The wide central passage originally carried a tramway both for distribution of feed and removal of manure to a covered storage pit.

necessary ventilation while preventing draughts, particularly around the head, which could prove unsettling to the cattle. They also allowed the area of window space to be minimised so that the internal temperature was more equable, the lighting more subdued and the stock more relaxed, especially in warmer months. These things mattered because the happier and healthier the stock were, the greater would be the gains in weight.

William Wilkinson, the Oxford architect, produced an interesting variant on the standard pattern by making a large covered yard the central feature of the livestock area, excavating its floor 4 ft beneath ground level and lining it with impermeable material. It would then operate as a giant receptacle harbouring all the waste from the other stock buildings and housing its own quota of cattle to keep everything well mixed. At the end of the season, a solid mass of manure several feet thick was available for digging out and distribution on the fields. The arrangement was featured first in

Model Farm, Shirburn in Oxfordshire, with roofs removed.
From the *Illustrated London News*, December 1857. The
steam-powered processing complex with associated crop
storage areas is at the top. Beneath, the larger unit
contains the main covered yard, divided into four, and
with its floor steeply sloping at both ends. It was
flanked on one side by stables for fourteen horses
and on the other by stalls for twelve cattle, six fatting
boxes and six pigsties.

Wilkinson's design of 1854 for the Earl of Macclesfield's home farm
at Shirburn, Oxfordshire.[15] This, one of the most advanced steadings
of the time, has benefited from enlightened modern management
and, by sympathetic conversion of parts of the site, is still able to
perform an agricultural function to the present day.

The original layout at Shirburn contained a fully mechanised
processing department powered by steam and served by a stackyard
tramway. Close by, the livestock areas were dominated by the central
covered yard, which was internally split into four 30 ft-square
sections. Into these drained the liquid manure from the surrounding
cart-horse stables, piggeries and feeding stalls, while the solid matter
was pushed through openings, fitted with sliding hatches, in the

dividing walls. Two other Wilkinson designs working on the same principle were the Longleat home farm of 1860 and the Northbrook Farm of 1858 on Sir Henry Dashwood's Kirtlington estate in Oxfordshire.[16] In each case, a difference in roof level between the covered yard and neighbouring buildings enabled a ventilation space to be created at eaves level while internal guttering on the lower section prevented any dilution of the manure.

Although the primary importance of cattle on farmsteads of this period is unmistakable, nevertheless great attention was also directed, for most of the same reasons, to the rearing and fattening accommodation for other forms of stock. Pigs, for example, needed dry, solid and well ventilated housing with sufficient space for movement if they were to thrive and perform up to standard as meat producers. The fattening boxes for pigs situated next to the covered yard at Northbrook Farm were in fact very similar in construction to those for cattle. At the front of each one was a trough with a hinged flap operated from the adjacent feeding passage. The flap was hitched forward while the trough was being filled to shut it off from the pigs, and pulled back when the feed was ready. Coleshill Farm incorporated pig boxes with sunken floors in the main fattening building, to which feed was conveyed by tramway. There was also a sheep-fattening house employing the sparred system of flooring, much debated at the time, which allowed all dung and urine to drop through gaps between the boards into a space beneath so that the floor itself remained sufficiently clean and dry for the sheep to tolerate.

For horses, the old convention of having lofts above stables for the supply of hay direct into racks below was now discredited in favour of buildings that were open to the rafters and so encouraged the freer circulation of air. There continued to be considerable variation in the internal arrangement of stables for working horses. In some the horses were tethered in lines without divisions, while in others single or double stalls or loose boxes were used. Over parts of Oxfordshire and other Midland counties the practice survived of feeding horses in stables but turning them out at night into their own yard. During the course of the period, informed opinion tended to prefer the line of single stalls with a loose box at the end for any horse that needed to be separated from the rest for reasons of illness or behavioural upset. By the last quarter of the century cast-iron stable fittings, from racks and

Late Victorian working horse stables at Brook Farm, Barkham
in Berkshire. Features include standard wooden partitions and
cast iron fittings, overhead ventilation designed to prevent
draughts, and gently sloping floor to a shallow drainage
gutter at the back.

mangers to division posts and railings, were freely available and
induced a stronger element of standardisation.

Between the peak of the high farming period in the 1860s and the
closing years of Victoria's reign, a significant change in emphasis did
occur to affect the type and quality of farmstead fixtures. The
economies necessitated by depression were reflected in the greater
advocacy of cheaper materials, with iron in particular being used
much more extensively, not simply for framing but for roofing and
cladding of walls as well. The storage of hay and corn beneath
corrugated-iron roofs supported by iron columns grew in popularity
because greater protection was provided from the vagaries of the
weather and the delicate art of building thatched stacks was avoided.
Specimen farm plans of the 1890s[17] retained the same basic relationship between storage, processing and livestock areas as had been
common to design theory forty years earlier. There was, however, a

69

notable absence not only of fixed threshing machinery but also of almost any discussion about the recommended power source for the feed-preparing equipment. The particular circumstances of the individual farm would now dictate whether either a portable or small stationary steam engine, or a simple horse gear, or one of the new oil engines was the most appropriate without the need for further debate. Lastly, while fattening stalls and boxes were still a feature of many farmsteads, there is no doubt that they were on the wane. The growing acceptance that small covered yards produced good-quality fat cattle and cheaper manure without the trouble of dung pits and underground tanks led to the steady demotion of perhaps the most vivid symbol of Victorian intensive farming.

3
Dairy Farms

Questions of physical layout and productive efficiency were not confined to the predominantly arable farms for they figured prominently in the thinking of leading dairy farms also. New ideas on the most appropriate form for a dairy farmstead began to appear in parallel with breeding improvements affecting the milking qualities of cows, scientific advances in the understanding of milk and its processed products, and social changes of great import for the future of the dairy business as a whole. In particular, the rapid expansion of urban centres was creating a colossal potential for increased milk consumption, which the railway network, as it grew, had the means to exploit. It had long been the case that agricultural areas in the immediate vicinity of cities were dominated by the urban market but, by the last quarter of the century, a farm within reasonable reach of a station in Derbyshire, Gloucestershire or Hampshire was quite likely to be sending daily supplies of milk down to London by rail.

The demand for milk in bulk came from a wide range of food-processing concerns in addition to the retail trade. When, therefore, Priory Farm at Beech Hill won the Berkshire Farm Prize Competition of 1882 it was disclosed that the milk from its 38 shorthorn cows was sold under contract to Huntley & Palmer, the Reading biscuit manufacturers, for an annual sum of around £1,000.[1] The ready market and secure returns that such arrangements gave were responsible for a shift in emphasis in many districts towards fresh milk at the expense of farmhouse cheesemaking. They also gave some protection from the foreign competition, which was proving remarkably adept at supplying an embarrassingly good-quality product to the British table at competitive prices. Since the first shipment in 1830, by the late 1870s over 50,000 tons of cheese were annually entering from America, where the factory system of production had been mastered early on. Total imports, close on 100,000 tons, represented 80 per cent of domestic production, while the figures for butter showed a parity, at about 90,000 tons, between home and

71

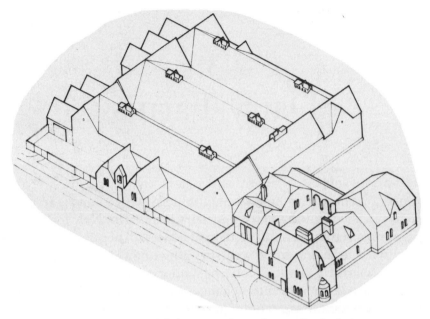

Bemerton Farm with its central cow house flanked above
by processing rooms and below by accommodation for pigs.
At the end, the two banks of pitched roofs are the site
of covered dung pits. Based on a drawing in J. Bailey
Denton's *Farm Homesteads of England*, 1863.

foreign supplies.[2] Much of the transformation that overtook dairy
farming in the Victorian period can be understood as a combined
response to these influences of the world market and the new
conditions brought about by a developing industrial society.

DESIGN OF DAIRY UNITS

Down on the farm, the view current in mid-century that well
appointed buildings contributed tangibly to the quality and quantity
of production at less cost in labour was taken up by the higher levels
of the dairying sector. In the late 1850s, Bemerton Farm on the
Wilton estate near Salisbury was endowed with the kind of dairy unit
designed to show the wisdom of this view to best effect.[3] Situated
outside the main dairying region of the county, which was further
west towards Warminster and Chippenham, the farm was principally
arable but contained in addition a 75-acre area of pasture and water
meadow. Accordingly, one side of the new covered steading was

occupied by the appropriate storage, processing and implement departments, while the sections immediately adjoining were given over to stalls for 36 dairy cows. These were grouped into two lines with feeding passages on either side and a wide throughway down the centre to allow for ease of access and milking. This part of the farmstead separated the dairy at one end from the covered manure pits at the other, so that the risk of milk being tainted by unpleasant odours was minimised. The remainder of the building was given over primarily to the housing of pigs, which as eager consumers of skimmed milk and whey, were an essential feature of the dairying economy everywhere.

A short cloistered passage linked the main complex with the dairy, next to which was a scullery, with hot water facilities, leading on to the dairyman's cottage. The not uncommon practice in southern districts of letting the cows to the dairyman at an annual fee was followed here at Bemerton. He was then responsible for the milking and retained the proceeds of all sales of milk products, while the tenant farmer supplied the feed, maintained the herd and made use of the manure. It might seem an unnecessarily complicated arrangement but the quality, and therefore the monetary value, of both butter and cheese were so dependent upon the skill and painstaking care of the dairy worker that it was in the interests of the farmer to furnish incentives in the hope of encouraging diligence.

Contemporary in date and cited as an example in a number of surveys at the time was the steading for the 320-acre Tattenhall Hall Farm in Cheshire.[4] One-third of the holding was arable, so brick-built Dutch barns for corn storage were provided at the top of the site, with threshing machinery close by to be driven by a portable engine. Additional processing operations, mainly to prepare a winter feed of steamed chaff and chopped roots, were powered by a small fixed steam engine. This was positioned behind the long transverse cow house which held a double row of stalls for 80 cows divided by a central feeding passage equipped with a tramway. On farms like these, where the cheesemaking dairy formed part of the house, the location of the house relative to the rest of the buildings was always a matter for compromise. Too close, and the smells of the farmyard would intrude, making the preservation of a sweet atmosphere in the dairy impossible. On the other hand, the milk did not benefit from being carried any great distance from the cows and the extra labour

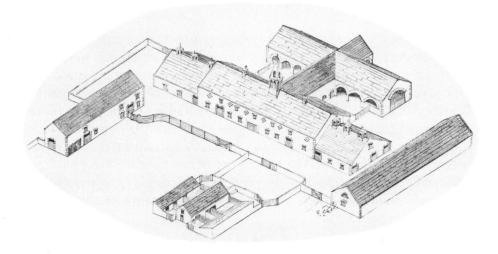

Tattenhall Hall Farm, Cheshire, dating from 1860 and
illustrated in J. P. Sheldon's *Dairy Farming*, 1878. From
the top, the site comprised a cruciform crop storage and
processing area, large central cow house, stables and cart
sheds in the buildings to the right, and a separate pig unit
in the foreground close to the house.

that this involved was unwelcome. At Tattenhall, the house was
allocated a sufficient degree of detachment while at the same time
being conveniently placed for the piggeries, into which the whey
could be channelled direct from the dairy. After a four-month curing
period, the cheese made here was sent for sale in London.

THE INFLUENCE OF PRINCE ALBERT

The most splendid dairy farmstead to appear in the great era of
building work at mid-century was that constructed in the Home
Park at Windsor for Prince Albert. He had gradually come to wield
effective control over the Castle estate of six farms, extending in
total to 2,400 acres and encompassing a broad variety of arable and
livestock husbandry. The keen interest that he genuinely showed in
agricultural improvements of all kinds, frequently demonstrated by
the new methods and equipment tried out on the farms, ensured that
his election as President of the Royal Agricultural Society in the year
of his death was based on much more than mere deference. Farm
buildings at Windsor achieved a level of priority comparable with

Cow house at Tattenhall Hall Farm, inside of which was a
double row of stalls for eighty cows. The higher central
portion contained a hay loft above. Winter feed was
prepared at the rear by mixing chaff with sliced roots
and steaming them in a specially devised room that
was supplied with waste steam from the adjacent
engine and boiler.

other leading estates so that not only was the dairy farm at Frogmore
completely replaced but also the steadings at the mixed-husbandry
Flemish and Shaw farms, the latter to the designs of George Dean.

The Windsor dairy farm had suffered a long spell of neglect prior to
Albert's taking command and the death of much of the herd from
disease in the mid-1840s made the construction of a more healthy
environment for the cattle an urgent necessity. A new site was
therefore chosen, plans drawn up by the resident architect, J. R.
Turnbull, and construction completed in 1855.[5] The result was as
majestic and impressive as it was practical for a farm complex that is
still able to provide extensive service in the very different agricultural
circumstances of today. Of central importance in the rectangular
layout was the main cow house, which Albert himself believed to be
the best in the world, fitted with a double row of stalls for 60 cows,
mainly Shorthorns. This was flanked on three sides by a combination
of sheds and yards for younger stock, while beyond were two lines of

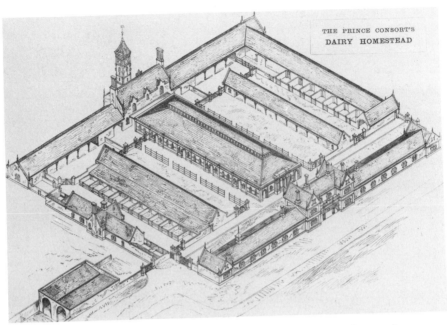

The Royal Dairy Farm at Windsor from *The Prince Consort's
Farms* by J.C. Morton, 1863. Running down the centre from
the feed store is the main cow house; to the right are
yards and pens for calving cows and their offspring;
to the left is a pig unit. At the bottom left is a covered
manure pit with tip cart access at one end for filling and
at the other, lower, end for emptying.

sties and ancillary feed-preparation areas for up to 20 breeding sows
of the noted Prince Albert herd of pigs.

Given the continuing development of the dairy industry in the last
quarter of the century, it is perhaps not so surprising that well
appointed dairy units were still appearing when the phase of rebuilding in the predominantly arable sector had long since passed its
peak. One example was the new complex designed for the home farm
on the Tyntesfield estate near Bristol in 1881. It occupied a split-level
site, the upper part of which was occupied by estate workshops and a
processing building containing equipment for chopping chaff, grinding meal and pulping roots, driven through line shafting from an
externally sited mobile steam engine. Chutes in the floor allowed feed
to be dropped through to the brick-arched storage bays beneath,
which formed part of the covered livestock building at the lower
level. Under this one roof were stalls for 20 cows set around two sides
of an internal yard and manure pit, a series of pens for calves, separate

76

The cow house at the Royal Dairy Farm. The middle doorway
led into the central feeding passage and the outer doors into
walkways at the rear of both lines of stalls.

boxes for the two bulls, and a line of piggeries. On the other side of
the roadway was constructed a circular thatched dairy adjacent to the
bailiff's house, while further along was another building specifically
for the curing of hams.

Further evidence of this steady interest in dairy arrangements, at
least towards the more exclusive end of the landowning spectrum,
may be found on the small Buckhold estate near Pangbourne in
Berkshire, which over the last two decades of the reign was dedicated
to the breeding and management of prize Jersey cattle.[6] The owner,
Dr Herbert Watney, had gone to considerable lengths to provide a
congenial environment for this delicate breed by providing an abun-
dance of well drained pasture, flanked by belts of trees for shelter, and
accommodation that was roomy, efficiently ventilated and clean. A
notable feature was the octagonal cow house, dating from the late
1880s, with a double circle of standings within its lofty interior.
Between them ran a tramway for horse-drawn trucks that removed all
waste materials both from here and from the other sheds and yards to
a site some distance away where the odour could cause no harm.

BUTTER

As much care was devoted here, and on other leading dairy farms, to the design and specification of the dairy itself as to the accommodation and comfort of the cattle. Older farmhouses very often had incorporated on their northern side a dairy that was dark, damp, badly ventilated and too close to stock areas to produce anything other than an inferior product. In the second half of the century, the chemical composition of milk came under close analysis and the scientific investigation of butter and cheesemaking processes led to a deeper understanding which in turn suggested practical improvements. The most notable contribution was made by Dr Augustus Voelcker, consultant chemist to the Royal Agricultural Society, who cut away much of the mystery of the dairy process by building up a scientific framework through many years of laboratory tests and experiments in the field.[7]

Voelcker clearly demonstrated the necessity of creating the correct physical conditions in order to achieve success and put cleanliness, ventilation and temperature control at the top of the list of crucial factors. Buttermaking required milk to stand for at least 24 hours before the cream could be skimmed and churned, while in cheesemaking it was common practice to leave the evening's milk in the dairy overnight and then to mix it with the following morning's supply prior to commencing the process. The ability to preserve milk in a pure, fresh state, whatever the season, was therefore an obvious requirement, for loss of condition at this stage had unavoidable effects upon the final quality. Temperature regulation was not simply a matter of inhibiting bacterial growth. Voelcker's experiments on the specific gravity of milk had appeared to show that 60°F was the optimum temperature for the rapid and efficient separation of cream. Later theories tended to attach greater weight to the range of temperature that the cooling milk fell through rather than any one magic figure. Nevertheless, the ideal of a uniform environment, cool in summer and not too cold in winter, was recognised on all sides and impinged very largely upon the design of buttermaking dairies in particular.

More traditional methods of retaining a cool atmosphere included lowering the floor of the dairy 2ft or more below ground level and

Inside the octagonal cow house at Buckhold at the
beginning of this century. Between the inner and outer
circles of standings for the Jersey herd ran the
tramway for distribution of feed and
removal of litter.

covering the roof with a material such as straw thatch that was a
very bad conductor of heat. However, the resulting problems of
dampness and the steady popularity of more durable roofing materials led progressively to the adoption of other solutions during the
century. That very elaborate precautions could be taken is evidenced
by the dairy at Park Farm, Woburn, which was built in the last year of
the reign. Here the milk room was cocooned inside an inner shell to
leave a wide insulating passage around three sides, fitted with vents
for the access of controlled ventilation. A boiler in the adjacent
scullery provided some warmth in winter as well as all the hot water
for the scalding apparatus that preserved the thorough cleanliness of
utensils.

Good results could be obtained without going to these lengths.
The small Victorian dairy at Bloomfield Hatch Farm in Berkshire, for
example, was a square structure set close to the kitchen of a much
older house but conveniently away from the intrusive smells of
the farmyard. The lofty ceiling, 12-inch-thick walls and sliding

ventilators ensured that in the heat of a summer's day the room would still be cool and airy. Supported on brick pillars around the plastered walls were stout slate shelves, on which the cream-separating dishes were placed. Slate was often used because it could be scrubbed clean and dried without difficulty and would always be cool to the touch. For similar reasons, the shallow separating pans were likely to be made either of glazed earthenware or, later in the century, of thin iron that had been pressed into the required shape and then tinned. The floor of this dairy was paved with heavy tiles to reinforce the feeling of coolness and small ventilating plates on the wall almost at ground level speeded the process of evaporation after washing.

The cool, surgical atmosphere of a buttermaking dairy, where the labour was mostly female and where an instantly recognisable product was created, made it a congenial stopping-place for the visitor unaccustomed to some of the other less agreeable sights and smells of the farm. On the home farm of a country estate, the dairy was an acceptable point of contact between agriculture and polite society; the lady of the house might well take more than a passing interest in its operations and would perhaps include it upon the itinerary of her weekend guests. In this case, its purpose was more than purely functional and its architectural style could be developed accordingly. The trend towards flamboyance in dairy design was already established well before the beginning of Victoria's reign. The pleasure grounds on the eastern side of Woburn Abbey, for example, still include the unique Chinese dairy built around 1794 and designed by Henry Holland, who had also been responsible for much work on the house. Inside, the effect was exquisite, with Chinese and Japanese porcelain dishes for the milk resting on black marble shelving and surrounded by patterns of mock bamboo. In Loudon's words, however, 'the dairy at Woburn is a fanciful structure in the Chinese style; but the plan and arrangement is not well calculated for keeping milk and butter cool and sweet'.[8] The real objective was to combine unquestioned utility with the desired visual flourish.

During the two decades that followed 1850, when investment in farm buildings was high, ornamental dairies figured most prominently in those remodelling schemes carried out on home farms. The use of glazed tiles on the walls to improve standards of cleanliness opened up a range of further opportunities for decoration which were not to be wasted. At Ardington in Oxfordshire, the new home farm

The ornamental dairy in Chinese style and dating from the end of the eighteenth century at Woburn Abbey in Bedfordshire.

The Ardington dairy now functions as a pottery and the milk room, still with its marble shelving, as a display area. On the tiled walls are examples of the pictorial panels by Henry Stacy Marks.

Thick marble shelving and densely patterned glazed tiles in
the dairy at Charlton Farm on the Tyntesfield estate in Avon.

complex on the estate of Colonel Lloyd-Lindsay, later Lord Wantage, included an attractive dairy constructed in mock Tudor style alongside a small watermill. A colonnaded entrance-way, where utensils could be stood to dry in safety, led into a milk room whose steeply pitched roof provided ample internal space for warm air to rise and escape through windows placed well above head height. The glazed tiling on the walls over the marble shelves bore a set of pictorial panels on the theme of Earth, Air, Fire and Water by Henry Stacy Marks, an artist with varied experience of work on country estates in the later Victorian period. The octagon often proved to be a practical and pleasing configuration for the milk rooms of dairies because it lent itself naturally to a tall, domed ceiling surmounted at its peak by a ventilator. The home farm, dating from the mid-1850s, on the Westonbirt estate in Gloucestershire contained one example while Charlton Farm, originally a tenanted farm on the Tyntesfield estate near Bristol, had another that was built in the 1860s, with a striking visual impact produced by a stained-glass-window effect and exotically patterned tiles.

Of all the Victorian ornamental dairies, the one to be found on the royal Windsor estate was, perhaps appropriately, entirely unsurpassed. An earlier structure dating from George III's time, with octagonal milk room, and adjacent churning area, was considered inadequate for the highest standards of production expected following completion of the dairy farm in 1855. So three years later a new dairy, designed by J. R. Turnbull, was built onto the north side of an existing bailiff's cottage, which now became quarters for the dairymaid. Prince Albert's intention in commissioning the work was clearly to create a magnificent showpiece and in this he succeeded although it cannot be said that utility was sacrificed for decoration along the way. The interior design was laid out by the sculptor John Thomas and made extensive use of highly patterned glazed tiles on floor and walls, where they were interspersed with bas-reliefs of majolica, specially produced for the purpose by Mintons of Birmingham. At the same time, cavity walling, a form of double glazing and a turret ventilator in the roof combined to maintain an equable temperature. Furthermore, the facility of channelling water along troughs beneath the marble tables and the presence of three fountains, two of majolica and the other of marble, saw to it that the heat of high summer would not intrude. In all, the 114 milk pans were

The Royal Dairy at Windsor, built on to an existing cottage
at the right which became the head dairymaid's house. Just
above the entrance arches are the words 'erected in the
twenty-first year of the reign of Her Majesty Queen Victoria'.
The tower of the Dairy Farm can be seen at the far right.

capable of holding 240 gallons of milk and careful records were kept
of daily quantities and the amounts of cream and butter produced. It
was an impressive fusion of art, agriculture and science.

CHEESE

Turning from butter to cheese is to move from one relatively simple
process with a tradition of architectural ornamentation to another
embodying more complex procedures and equipment but fewer
decorative features because the prestigious home farms were less
likely to be involved. Differences in method, underlying soil, type of
pasture and so on had combined to form the familiar regional English
cheeses, the precise taste and quality of which could vary from farm
to farm. Derby cheese, for example, was a locally popular, nourishing,
but unpretentious product that remained largely outside the circles

84

Milk room of the Royal Dairy at Windsor, perfectly preserved.

of polite society, whereas Leicester was regarded as the finest cheese England had to offer and, judging by its price of up to £1 a cwt more than any other variety, a delicacy suited to even the richest table. Cheesemaking was not, of course, left unaffected by the changes taking place throughout Victorian agriculture. Drainage and the application of fertilisers to pasture were common improvements which, in a county such as Leicestershire, might increase cattle densities and boost yields while at the same time diminishing the special distinctive quality the cheese had acquired from the old grassland. Competition from foreign imports certainly persuaded some areas, including parts of Gloucestershire, to give up production of a cheese that would never rise above good average quality and concentrate instead on the liquid milk trade. For those willing to participate, technological and scientific development could not only make the physical work of cheesemaking a little easier but also serve to impose a measure of standardisation upon techniques that made the regional variations seem more homogeneous. To illustrate the effects of change of this sort by the later nineteenth century, just two cheesemaking regions, Somerset and Cheshire, will be examined here.

Joseph Harding (1805–76) of Marksbury in Somerset

CHEESEMAKING IN SOMERSET

In Somerset, Victorian cheesemaking is firmly linked with the name of Joseph Harding of Marksbury near Bath. His achievement was first to systematise and then to popularise an efficient, modern and easily understood method of producing the traditional product, Cheddar, in such a way that it was able to assume a more uniform identity in the eyes of makers and consumers alike. The dairy at the rear of the house at Marksbury consisted of separated areas for making, pressing and curing the cheese, together with space for accommodating the water-heating apparatus. This consisted of a boiler from which hot water could be passed into the false bottom of the cheese tub, to warm the contents, and also into pipes that ran around both the making-room and the curing-room above. Two important purposes were thus achieved: the cheesemaking process could proceed at the correct temperatures without too much difficulty, and the curing-room could be maintained within the optimum range of 50–60°F in the winter months to absorb satisfactorily the 2lb of moisture per ton given off each day by newly made cheese.[9] In addition, the boiler gave abundant quantities of hot water for the thorough cleansing of all equipment.

At Marksbury, the Cheddar process began when the milk from the morning and previous evening's milking was combined in the cheese tub and the temperature raised, by means of the hot-water jacket, to about 80°F. The correct amount of rennet, made from the stomachs of Irish calves, was then added, together with a quantity of sour whey, and the whole allowed to stand for an hour while the milk coagulated. The resulting curd was carefully cut into squares with a long-bladed knife and then turned and divided with the aid of a cream-skimming dish. Further reduction, by the paddle-shaped breaker, left the curd in small lumps the size of coins, ready for scalding in the tub at a temperature of 100°F. Following a period of stirring, the mixture was allowed to stand before the whey was drawn off into another vat to be set for buttermaking and the remainder was piped away to the piggeries. Meanwhile, the curd, having cooled down and gained the requisite level of acidity, was ground in a hand-powered mill and mixed with salt at the rate of 2lb for each hundredweight. It was then packed into a mould and placed in the lever-operated press for up to three days. It was then removed, wrapped in bandages and placed on a shelf in the curing-room, where it was regularly turned over the course of the three months that the new cheese took to mature into a ripe, full-flavoured Cheddar.

This, in outline, was the technique discussed in pamphlets and lectures at mid-century, and taught to the many pupils and visitors who made their way to Marksbury. The general standard of cheese-making in Somerset and surrounding counties benefited as a result and knowledge of the system travelled further afield to other dairying districts in England and Scotland, and even overseas as well. Harding's daughter helped by winning many prizes at English shows and a gold medal at the 1865 French Exhibition for her cheeses made on the same principle. She was based with her husband, George Gibbons, a few miles away at Tunley Farm, a 200-acre holding on the Camerton estate. Here was constructed in the early 1870s an almost completely new set of buildings featuring housing for 33 Shorthorn cattle that

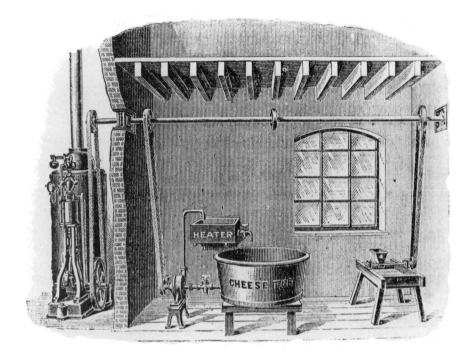

Equipment for a cheddar cheese dairy built in the 1880s. The small vertical steam engine drives a centrifugal pump for raising milk or whey into the heater, and also the curd mill on the right. Steam from the boiler is passed through the double bottom of the heater to warm the contents and in addition supplies hot water and steam jets for the cleansing of all utensils.

was equipped with two tramways, one for the supply of feed and the other for removal of manure. Chaff-cutting and milling machinery was powered by a small steam engine installed in an older barn, while the water supply for the whole farm was raised by hydraulic ram from a spring lower down the valley. In the dairy premises behind the house, one cheese weighing anything from 70 to 120lb was made per day from the milk of the previous 24 hours. From the whey about 15lb of butter was made each week, leaving the rest to be fed to the small herd of Berkshire pigs kept close by. Mrs Gibbons conducted the cheesemaking operations herself, with the help of a girl, and four women were employed to do all the milking at the rate of one shilling each per day.[10]

CHEESEMAKING IN CHESHIRE

In Cheshire and adjoining counties, the grazing pastures on the underlying new red sandstone formations gave to the cheese its distinctive and highly valued qualities. Cheesemaking was organised on a large scale, producing an estimated 12,000 tons in 1845,[11] and on the bigger estates, notably those of Lord Crewe and the Duke of Westminster, led to some superb dairy farmsteads where the very latest in advanced Victorian techniques were employed. Three primary methods of making the cheese had been identified, known respectively as the early-, medium- and late-ripening processes, although as always the precise details varied from farm to farm.[12] One system, commonly practised on the medium-ripening method, concentrated cheesemaking into the months from April to September, when quality was at its best, and then relied upon the steady income from liquid milk sales for the remainder of the year. This cheese was made once a day, combining as before the morning's milk with that of the previous evening and employing the jacketed vat as a means of obtaining suitable temperature control. A distinctive element of the Cheshire dairy was the cheese oven set within brickwork and heated by warm air rising up an adjacent kitchen or other chimney. Here the curd, after being milled, salted and placed into a mould, was left overnight at a temperature of at least 90°F to speed the removal of the whey. Following four or five days in the press, the new cheese was greased to prevent the rind from cracking and then dressed in bandages for the curing stage, which lasted for a further two months or more. Temperature at this stage was still important and the better equipped cheese rooms were warmed by hot-water piping running around the walls. Such was the size of Cheshire cheeses, weighing anything up to 100lb, that hand-operated lifts were recommended for raising them to the curing-room at first-floor level. One of these remains in the dairy wing behind the house at Stapleford Hall Farm, Tarvin, where a milking herd of 87 Shorthorns was kept on the 300-acre holding at the end of the century.[13]

A good impression of an advanced Cheshire dairy farm can be gained from Spurstow Hall at Tarporley, where detailed records of output were kept from the 1880s.[14] This was a tenanted farm of 367 acres on Lord Crewe's estate, with substantial buildings constructed in 1873 for the accommodation of cattle and a dairy complex close to the house equipped with a small steam engine and a system for pumping whey direct to troughs in the piggery. In 1892, the 104 Shorthorns in milk that year produced a little over 26,000 gallons for sale and a further 31,000 gallons from which more than 13 tons of cheese were made. Taking into account all other factors, including the 475lb of whey butter that was also made and the number of calves that were reared and sold, the total financial yield was calculated at £1,779 12s at an average of almost £17 2s per cow. In fact, this had not been a good season in comparative terms because the returns for each year of the previous decade had been higher and on two occasions the average had exceeded £20 per cow.

Two farms from the Duke of Westminster's Eaton estate will serve to summarise the best of farmhouse cheesemaking in Cheshire. At Cotton Abbotts, 282 acres of pasture supported 105 milking cows in 1893 with a production average of over 5cwt of cheese per head over the year. It was reported that during the peak summer period five cheeses of 70lb each were being made in the dairy every day.[15] The buildings for cows and young stock were constructed in the 1880s and included rows of stalls separated by a wide passageway on the ground floor and hay 'tallats', or stores, above. A substantial house for the tenant, dated 1872, incorporated a dairy at the rear where a small vertical steam engine drove whey pumps for the piggeries, powered churning and curd-grinding equipment, and also supplied hot water for all associated cleansing and heating purposes.

A little further south at Aldford was Lea Farm, with 353 acres and 120 shorthorn-cross milkers. Here considerable expense was incurred to give the steading the same mix of agricultural utility and physical grandeur that was the distinctive style of the estate.[16] The main cow unit was constructed in 1892 to replace some earlier buildings that had been burnt down. As a result, the internal walls dividing the hay and corn stores on the first floor were continued up through the roof structure in order to create separate compartments that would impede the spread of another fire. A common practice in the area was to employ casual Irish labourers during the peak summer months and on this farm a room was provided for them over the harness store in the stable block. The house, built in 1875, was large enough to accommodate three live-in farm workers and five domestic servants in addition to the farmer's family. Beyond the kitchen at the

Behind the house at Cotton Abbots Farm on the Eaton
estate in Cheshire, the late nineteenth-century steam boiler
survives though without the small vertical engine that was
mounted on the frame next to it. Steam was used to drive
the water pump in the foreground and also supplied all
the needs of the cheesemaking dairy within.

91

back ran an extended dairy, with the full complement of steam-powered equipment, where the farmer's wife and her three dairy-maids produced cheese of the highest quality.

This was the zenith that farmhouse cheesemaking reached in the late Victorian period. However, no matter how impressive the operations run by the leading farms, it was still essentially a system based on small units of production and dependent upon a necessarily labour-intensive, and therefore expensive, process only imperfectly suited to the demands of an expanding mass market. Centralisation of production into cheese factories, leaving the farm free to concentrate on its milk yield, was a logical rationalisation, indicating the path of future development. The first steps, indeed, had already been taken; factory cheesemaking, having been pioneered overseas, first came to England in 1870.

4
Farmhouses and Cottages

The Victorian farmer considered that he deserved a better standard of housing and the labourer was looking for a decent roof over his head. For the one it was a matter of social position, for the other a case of desperate need. Not all were successful for at the end of the century there were still plenty of old run-down farmhouses and a depressing level of miserable squalor was not difficult to find in the rural labouring community. Nevertheless, things had been changing and the visible proof is still there in the countryside today. Of course, the showpiece farms with their near-palatial residences and the estate villages with their streets of neat cottages attract the attention and can, too hastily, be dismissed as a superficial gloss on a much more daunting reality. The fact is that many farmhouses were either entirely rebuilt or substantially modified in the period, and a broad scattering of post-1850 semi-detached or terraced farm cottages still exists today. In part, at least, the social requirements of the farmer were met, and the sensitivities of social concern for the labourer were eased, by landowners responding to their obligations of stewardship with more programmes of building and modernisation.

A SUITABLE HOUSE FOR A SUITABLE TENANT

There was also a weighty element of self-interest at work, which the architectural writers were not slow to seize upon. Thus Charles Waistell, when pressing the importance of cottages, referred to the labouring classes as 'living engines' that needed proper maintenance in order to function efficiently for their employers.[1] In the same way, farms that were provided with well arranged buildings, houses included, would attract tenants of the requisite calibre, whose profitable and responsible husbandry would be beneficial to the landowner. A 500-acre farm could absorb £5,000 of a tenant's capital, and a 1,000-acre farm twice this, so it was necessary to attract men of some

93

Design for a farmhouse from Francis Goodwin's *Rural Architecture* of 1835. To the left of the entrance porch were a substantial dining-room and parlour, while the projecting wing to the right contained an office on the ground floor from which work in the farmyard could be observed.

considerable financial and social standing. The old style of house, with farmer and servants enjoying a rough coexistence in the large frugal kitchen, was not for them. They were not so much sons of the soil as a new breed of commercial managers – well educated, sometimes having successful alternative careers in business or one of the professions, and expecting to surround themselves with at least the same degree of domestic comfort and refinement as was enjoyed by their urban counterparts at the forefront of industry.

The architecture of the villa had already made its appearance on the farmstead before the accession of Victoria. Interest was fuelled by the pattern books of specimen plans produced by architects hoping to gather new commissions. The second edition of the book by the London-based architect Francis Goodwin, for example, came out in 1835 and contained designs for all manner of buildings to ornament the country estate, including farmhouses, which he believed were best constructed in the Old English style.[2] J.C. Loudon's *Encyclopaedia of Cottage, Farm and Villa Architecture* was an exhaustive compendium drawing upon the work of architects and designers throughout the country and depicting the layout of farmhouse and cottage in almost any style that might be required. In his words, the book would

'not only enable those who wish either to build or to furnish, to express more clearly, to the architect or upholsterer, those wants which they already have; but it will elicit new ones, of which they had previousiy no idea, and which the architect, the builder and the upholsterer will be called upon to supply.'[3]

From the first version of 1833 and on through subsequent editions, the book became a reference manual that was still in circulation in the drawing-office and country house during the period of renewed vigour in new building work twenty years later.

So the ideal house for the forward-looking Victorian tenant farmer was in most respects distinguishable from the large surburban villa only by the extra offices – such as dairy, brew-house or apple store – that agriculture demanded. On some estates, such as Wilton in Wiltshire, where wholesale modernisation schemes were undertaken, the new houses provided for tenants were by any standard substantial buildings worthy of the social aspirations of the occupant. While being close enough to give the farmer a view into the yards, the house was not an integral part of the farmstead arrangement; rather, a measure of detachment was maintained so that it could present a quite different and refined face to the world at large. Illustrating this dual role, the house at Castle End Farm, on J.C. Garth's small Berkshire estate at Twyford, is dated 1857 and from the side was in reasonable visual contact with the working areas of the farmstead; but at the front a quite separate graceful driveway swept round to the main entrance for the reception of guests and visitors well away from the sights and smells of agriculture.

The dividing line between a suitably proportioned house for a tenant and an over-generous costly luxury could be crossed quite easily when ambitious schemes ran away with themselves. George Dean acknowledged that the house he had designed for one of the Holkham tenants, T.M. Hudson, was considered by some to have

Farmhouse from J.C. Loudon's *Encyclopaedia of Cottage,
Farm and Villa Architecture*, 1846 edition. The house was
built in the early 1830s on Charles Barclay's estate near
Dorking in Surrey. Downstairs the principal rooms were a
parlour, dairy, scullery and pump room with four
good sized bedrooms above.

been good enough for the eldest son of the landowner himself.
Nevertheless, he insisted 'that it is not too good for the occupier, nor
for many other Holkham tenants, who justly take rank among the
first agriculturists of the country, and who occupy some of the largest
farms in it'.[4] The biggest might deserve the best, but on the smaller
holding the social expectations of the farmer could be well in excess
of the status merited by the income from his farm.

Bailey Denton attempted to codify the degree of restraint necessary by producing a sliding scale of costs and specifications for houses
matched to specific grades of farm.[5] It was not so much a simple
question of relating house size to farm size, for the tenant of a small
farm might very well have as large a family, and therefore need as
much space, as the tenant of a much bigger farm. The correlation was
instead to be between the level of extras or refinements incorporated
into the plan and the amount of tenant capital required to stock and
run the farm effectively. On this basis, the kind of house recommended at the bottom of the scale, for farms of 200 acres, would still

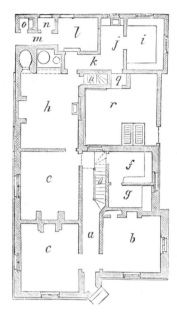

a. Passage.

b. Living room or office.

c. Living room.

d. Front stairs.

e. Kitchen.

f. Larder.

g. Store closet.

h. Wash-house.

i. Dairy.

j. Scullery.

k. Passage.

l. Coals.

m. Passage.

n. Ashes.

o. Privy.

p. Back stairs.

q. Porch.

r. Courtyard.

Downstairs rooms at Toothill farmhouse from J. Bailey
Denton's *Farm Homesteads of England*, 1863.

be a large and relatively expensive structure if it were provided with the standard complement of living and working areas. Denton's example in this category was the house he himself designed in 1861 for the 200-acre Toothill Farm on the Broadlands estate in Hampshire. On either side of the front entrance were two day rooms – one of which could be used as an office if necessary – where the farmer and his wife could surround themselves with the smart décor of Victorian consumer society. Behind was a large kitchen operating as a multipurpose living and eating area during the working day, and beyond this a service unit composed of washhouse, coal-house, dairy and scullery arranged at right angles around a courtyard and with a cellar below. There were five bedrooms upstairs and, following common practice, a second or back staircase led from the washhouse directly into the maid's bedroom.

Progressing up the hierarchy, a suitable house for a farm of 500 acres or so would be a little bigger with the principal living area for the family concentrated on two spacious ground-floor rooms, one of

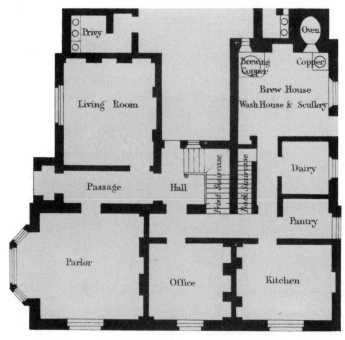

Downstairs rooms at Cedars Farm, Lower Boddington from
J. Bailey Denton's *Farm Homesteads of England*, 1863.

which was often referred to as the parlour. Upstairs, there might be
six large bedrooms and a separate water closet to supplement the
privy that was usually tucked away behind the kitchen or scullery.
Little Almshoe farmhouse, on the estate of William Dashwood at St
Ippollitts near Hitchin, was constructed along these lines in 1855.
The entrance hall and staircase divided the two living-rooms on one
side from the kitchen and dairy on the other, and a passage led to the
scullery, coal-house and brew-house beyond. Many permutations of
the same essential arrangement were possible. Dating from this
period, Cedars Farm at Lower Boddington in Northamptonshire
split the living and service areas into two parallel wings joined at the
centre by the hall, staircase and farm office. The house was built of
stone under a Welsh slate roof for the sum of £900 using the direct
labour of Earl Spencer's estate, of which it formed a part.

On the largest farms rising to 1,000 acres, the specifications were
extended still further and the house moved into the country residence bracket, to be compatible with the financial and social status of
the tenant. Apart from a more sumptuous external appearance, other

distinguishing features included a rigid delineation of the living areas into dining-room and drawing-room, both highly furnished and enjoying attractive views of the garden from ornamental window bays. There would also be a breakfast room for informal daily use and a separate farm office, while overhead were six or seven bedrooms, two probably having dressing-rooms attached. Perhaps the most telling identifying factor was the inclusion of accommodation at the service end of the house for the riding and driving horses and family gig. The smaller farm would have these quartered in a convenient part of the farmstead itself but the bigger house was self-contained to the point of operating normally without reference to the farm at all.

Manor Farm at Horsington in Somerset was built well up to these standards in 1877.[6] At the time it was only a 600-acre holding on Thomas Dodington's Horsington estate but a programme of enlargement was in progress to merit the complete rebuilding of house and farmstead under the direction of the Clevedon architect, Robert Shout. The very substantial cost of £9,000 reflected the high specification of the work, the difficulties of building on a sloping site and the fact that a water-driven machinery block was located further down the hill. The six-bedroomed house included a stable yard to the side and a smaller kitchen yard at the rear, where there was a fully equipped cheesemaking dairy with a store for cheeses above, next to the manservant's bedroom. Beyond, and across a driveway, were the main farm buildings, comprising piggeries, cow stalls and fattening house arranged around three sides of an open yard. These were well to the rear of the house and, since the domestic apartments were all facing the opposite way, it is evident that the golden rule, so frequently repeated twenty or thirty years earlier, that the farmer should have a clear view into the farmstead from his sitting-room, had been forsaken in favour of more pleasing vistas of the garden.

In the opinion of some, this subtle change was indicative of a deeper underlying social transformation that threatened to place the lifestyle of the farmer at a remote distance from the real world of farming. The larger farmers, the men of capital and substance, had always been in a position to manage their affairs through intermediaries and turn instead to the sporting and social pleasures of country life. What provoked comment in the second half of the century was an apparent tendency for parts of the middling group of farmers to aspire to something of the same and be seduced by the

Parting of the ways for farmstead and house at Manor Farm,
Horsington, in Somerset. The lower extension at the back
of the house comprised dairy, bake-house and riding stables
arranged around an open yard.

The milk room in the dairy at Manor Farm, Horsington.

fashions and conventions of polite society when their agricultural incomes could ill afford it. One acute observer of the countryside in the period was the journalist and author Richard Jefferies, who penned some particularly caustic descriptions of what was at least a popular impression if not a universal trend:

'The "civilisation" of the town has, in fact, gone out and taken root afresh in the country. There is no reason why the farmer should not be educated; there is no reason why his wife should not wear a sealskin jacket, or the daughter interpret Beethoven. But the question arises, has not some of the old stubborn spirit of earnest work and careful prudence gone with the advent of the piano and the oil painting? While wearing the dress of a lady, the wife cannot tuck up her sleeves and see to the butter, or even feed the poultry, which are down at the pen across "a nasty dirty field".'[7]

Jefferies' implication was that the farmers' pursuit of an alternative life was partly responsible for the economic difficulties being experienced by agriculture at the time. But perhaps in any age the simple, good, honest, down-to-earth and hard-working farmer seems to have been an inhabitant only of the past.

THE LABOUR FORCE

For a majority of the farm labour force, the main preoccupation was rather different. How to maintain something resembling regular employment, sufficient to feed and house the family, without falling prey to the degradation of the workhouse, was what really mattered. Few labouring men were in a position to own their own homes except through a benign accident of fortune or the exercise of outstanding thrift coupled with the possession of an additional craft or manual skill to raise the income level. Decent rented accommodation was in short supply but who was going to sink money into building cottages worthy of human habitation when simple arithmetic showed that the average farm wage was too low to support an economic rent? This was the nub of a problem that persisted throughout the nineteenth century, notwithstanding the effects of legislation or the efforts of benevolent individuals and organisations to overcome it. To live in

101

conditions of appalling discomfort, both insanitary and overcrowded, was by no means uncommon at the end of the Victorian reign, even though some considerable advances had been made and the administrative mechanism of social improvement in the countryside was beginning to roll.

The Victorians were assiduous investigators into the health and well-being of the rural population and their official reports are the source of much startling detail. In 1867, for example, the Commission on the Employment of Children, Young Persons and Women in Agriculture included the matter of cottage accommodation within its terms of reference. By now the scarcity of, albeit unsuitable, housing was less severe in some areas because a marked exodus from the countryside in search of a more promising future in the towns and overseas was already under way. For those remaining, it was not merely the physical but also the moral and spiritual evils provoked by the standard of accommodation that aroused most comment, especially as written submissions on local conditions were often supplied by churchmen. In their view, things were worst in the so-called open villages, where desperate people congregated to pay heavily for room in overcrowded hovels owned in many cases by local tradesmen and petty speculators. By contrast, the atmosphere of the closed parish, where all or most of the housing was owned and controlled by the landed proprietor, could be one of comparative comfort and civilised calm.

Assistant Commissioner the Reverend James Fraser, reporting on the counties of Norfolk, Essex, Sussex and Gloucester, had found the wretched consequences of too many people sharing the same unwholesome space quite shocking:

'Modesty must be an unknown virtue, decency an unimaginable thing, where, in one small chamber, with the beds lying as thickly as they could be packed, father, mother, young men, lads grown and growing girls – two and sometimes three generations – are herded promiscuously; where every operation of the toilette and of nature – dressings, undressings, births, deaths – is performed by each within the sight or hearing of all; where children of both sexes, to as high an age as 12 or 14, or even more, occupy the same bed; where the whole atmosphere is sensual, and human nature is degraded into something below the level of the swine.'[8]

102

The Norfolk estate village of Great Bircham, where neat
groups of well appointed cottages predominate.

From Norfolk, the Reverend Hare described his parish of Docking,
an open village of about 300 cottages, many of whose inhabitants
trudged out daily to labour on farms scattered widely over the
surrounding area. Citing the example of a one-bedroomed dwelling
containing a family of six children and one grandchild in addition to
the parents, he blamed the thoroughly inadequate housing as 'the
root of all immorality and much of the ill-health in this parish'.[9]
Towards the end of the century, the overall picture was still dis-
couraging. William Little, in his summary for another Royal Commission of 1893 touching on the same subject, concluded that 'the
accommodation provided in respect of the number, size and comfort
of the rooms, the sanitary condition, and the water supply are
lamentably deficient generally and require amendment'.[10]
   It was indeed a black picture, the memory of which must be
retained in order to set the undoubted Victorian achievement in
cottage building into perspective. Neat, well designed cottages from

this period are an attractive and prominent element of today's countryside principally because they have survived relatively intact whereas the much more numerous lower grade of housing has either been swept away or recycled into an acceptable twentieth-century form. They represent an idealised approach to the problem that certainly helped to alleviate the rural housing crisis but could not actually be extended far enough to solve it. Nevertheless, many thousands of decent homes were built for labouring families during the reign and, whatever the qualifying statements, it was still a very considerable step forward, the like of which had never been seen before. Thus, alongside the misery of Docking, the 1867 Commission listed also the nearby village of Great Bircham, where most of the property was owned by the Marquis of Cholmondeley of Houghton Hall. The Reverend Winckworth reported that

'there is a general improvement going on here. The cottages are well built; rooms generally 10ft square, some are 12ft, and lofty, with windows made to open, and back doors and windows. Good drainage, and we are very free from fevers and general diseases. There are to be 30 new cottages, and 15 rebuilt, within three years, all to have three bedrooms.'[11]

FARMWORKERS' COTTAGES

On the landed estates, there was nothing new in the construction of cottages for in the eighteenth century it was not uncommon for them to figure, directly or indirectly, in ambitious landscaping schemes. The Norfolk village of New Houghton, for example, with its twenty-five plain but adequate houses, was built in 1729 on the approach road to the Hall to replace an earlier settlement that had stood in the way of Walpole's plans for an extensive park surrounding his residence. By the end of that century, fanciful cottages in picturesque style had become a fashionable device for adorning an estate and collections of specimen designs were widely published. John Nash's Blaise Hamlet near Bristol, dating from 1810 and with fairytale thatched cottages, each one different from the next, acted as a guiding light for some later model villages. Among them were numbered the Duke of Devonshire's Edensor, close by Chatsworth, of 1838, and Somer-

Entrance lodges on the Englefield estate in Berkshire
dating from the 1860s.

leyton in Suffolk, which was built by the railway entrepreneur Samuel
Morton Peto in 1856, a few years before he suffered bankruptcy,
brought on partly by overindulgence in the embellishment of his
estate. The survival of this tradition was most clearly expressed in the
ornamental gate lodges and keepers' or other cottages within the
home park that continued to spring up throughout the Victorian
period.

It is important not to confuse these charming, if somewhat
eccentric creations with the provision of a more utilitarian brand of
housing for the farm and estate labour force. Interest gathered
momentum in the 1840s, partly because official investigations had
already begun to make some shocking revelations about rural living
conditions,[12] but also because the health and well-being of the
workers were elements in the theory of farm improvement. The
incongruity of devoting such care and attention to the accommodation of livestock in new farmsteads while labourers continued
to live in pitiful squalor was not lost on enlightened opinion and
helped to force a climate of change. It was reflected in the lengthy debate that took root in the agricultural press of the day, accompanied

by a wealth of advice on how best to combine cheapness of construction with the physical and moral health of the occupants.

One of the objects of the Royal Agricultural Society, according to its charter, was 'to promote the comfort and welfare of labourers and to encourage the improved management of their cottages and gardens'. Give a man a good home, so the argument ran, and you give him the self-respect to lead an honest, upright life with less need for recourse to the alehouse. To this end, the Society periodically offered prizes for essays on the subject published in its journal. One of the contributors, J. Young Macvicar, produced detailed plans and costings in 1849 of semi-detached labourers' cottages each having a pantry, kitchen and scullery on the ground floor while above were three bedrooms, so that sons and daughters could be separated and the parents still have their own room.[13] The principal source of heating was the kitchen range, equipped with both a water boiler and an oven, which was able to warm the upstairs as well by virtue of the central chimney that ran up the wall dividing the two cottages.

To the rear of the house in Macvicar's plan were a coal-house, privy, ashpit and pigsty. Opinion was divided on the advisability of keeping a pig so close: some believed that on health grounds it was only asking for trouble while others pointed to the beneficial effects on the family diet. There was more agreement on the wisdom of attaching large gardens, up to half an acre in this case, for a vegetable plot would both compensate the labourer for the low wages he received and also provide a useful outlet for his free time. Care should be taken, however, not to allow too large an area that would absorb a disproportionate effort at the expense of the labourer's paid employment on the farm. Along with these practical details of arrangement came also much forthright advice on household management. French Burke was clear about the woman's role, for

'to attach a man to his home it is necessary that home should have attractions; and if his wife is a slattern, everything will go wrong; but if she is industrious, thrifty and good-tempered, cleanly in her person and her cottage, all will then go right. She will forego tea and gossip, she will put everything in the neatest order; her little fire trimmed and her hearth swept for the reception of her husband on his return from labour. Whatever may have been her cares during the day, she will meet him with the smile of welcome.'[14]

Front and side views of a design for a pair of labourers'
cottages by J. Young Macvicar. From the *JRASE* of 1849.

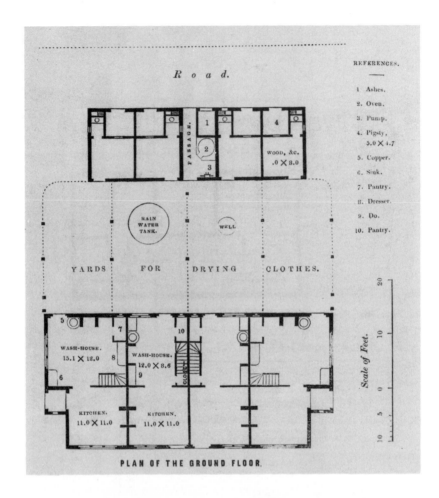

PLAN OF THE GROUND FLOOR.

Plan of a four cottage unit, one of many erected on the Duke of Bedford's Woburn estate. Each has a wash-house and kitchen on the ground floor with a pigsty, wood store and privy in the out-house and shared access to a bread oven. The two inner cottages have two bedrooms and the outer ones three. From the *JRASE* of 1849.

No doubt this and similar articles in the same vein meant well.

The tenth Duke of Bedford, writing in 1897, believed that no subject was more important to the landowner than cottage management because 'good and comfortable cottages, in which the decencies and dignity of human life may be maintained, generally imply that they are inhabited by good and efficient labourers'.[15] In this he was following the example set by the seventh duke in mid-century, who had been responsible for the replacement of many inadequate dwellings with the cottages that remain on the Bedford estates today. They were built in blocks of twos, threes, fours and sixes with the accommodation of individual units ranging in extent and pattern to take account of different sizes of family grouping.[16] Not only was it desirable to allocate a larger cottage to the labourer with growing children to reduce overcrowding and separate the sexes at bedtime; it was also prudent to have smaller versions available for those with fewer mouths to feed lest they succumb to the temptation of taking in lodgers with all the moral dangers that that implied.

In practice, the Bedford system comprised a mixture of semi-detached cottages each with a single bedroom and combinations of two- and three-bedroomed dwellings in the multiple blocks. Effective management demanded a degree of mobility on the part of the tenants, particularly from the larger to the smaller units once the children had left the parental home. William Bear's report on the Poor Law Union of Woburn for the 1893 Royal Commission on Labour included the complaints of one tenant who

'had to leave the commodious cottage he occupied at 1*s* 9*d* a week, although he was quite willing to pay that rent, as he wished to remain where he had lived for many years; but as his family had grown up and left him, he and wife were obliged to move into a smaller cottage at a lower rent.'[17]

It was not always an easy task to arrange the transfers amicably so for the cottage foreman employed by the estate this was one of his more delicate duties, calling for considerable tact and understanding if good communal relations were to be maintained.

The cottages as constructed contained on the ground floor a kitchen with a cooking-range and a washhouse with copper, sink and pantry. Beyond was a back yard and at the bottom a pigsty, coal-store and privy for each house, together with a shared ashpit, bread oven and water pump. To ensure adequate ventilation upstairs, bedrooms one and two were equipped with fireplaces, while a vent let into the chimney passage was considered sufficient for third bedrooms. By the end of the century a number of alterations had been made to the original arrangements, partly in response to new sanitary regulations and partly as a result of experience coupled with changing living patterns. The inclusion of the washhouse within the main structure, for example, was found to be unsatisfactory because of the dampness that was caused and because of the other activities, such as the preparation of pig feed, that tended to go on there. It was preferable then to make space for it in an enlarged service block at the rear, where, in turn, the communal oven was now redundant through the growing habit of labouring families to buy in bread rather than make their own. With this change, the revised configuration inside the house took the form of living-room, pantry and kitchen instead of the previous kitchen and washhouse.

COSTS, WAGES AND RENTS

The Dukes of Bedford were not alone amongst aristocratic proprietors in denying that cottage building could or should be a paying proposition. Rather, it was to be regarded as one of the obligations incumbent upon owners of landed property. Many of the wealthy industrialists and businessmen who were buying up country estates for the social prestige that went with them adopted the same principle, often with zeal. H. J. Little in his 1878 survey of the farm labourer singled out this sector for extra praise, 'for no people have been more ready than the nouveaux riches, when purchasers of land, to accept the responsibility connected with its possession, and to improve the condition of the cottages of the poor'.[18] It is true that the pursuit of economic viability led amongst other things to proposals, albeit based on some rather dubious figures, for a £60 cottage, an £85 cottage and a certain amount of experimentation with alternative materials such as concrete.[19] The simple truth, however, was that the minimum cost of building a pair of three-bedroomed cottages, to a standard acceptable to the Inclosure Commissioners for the purposes of a loan, was somewhere between £250 and £300, depending upon local circumstances. In Bailey Denton's view, and taking the higher of these two figures, a rent of £18 per year or *3s 6d* per cottage per week would be necessary for the owner to cover his costs adequately.[20] A labouring man in the 1860s struggling to bring up a family on a wage ranging from around ten shillings in southern England up to fifteen shillings or so in northern areas could not be realistically expected to pay a rent of this magnitude.

Mid nineteenth-century terraced cottages in the village of
Thorney, Cambridgeshire, on the Duke of Bedford's estate.

On the Bedford estates, rents were normally lower than the going
rate for inferior accommodation in surrounding villages. So the
weekly charge at Woburn for three-bedroomed cottages with a
quarter of an acre of garden was only 1s 4d, when the cost of building
in 1865 had been £350 a pair. The duke himself produced tables in
1897 showing that the rents collected from 768 cottages on his estates
in Bedfordshire and Buckinghamshire did not even cover maintenance and other costs, with the result that there was an annual
deficit of a little over £1,000.[21] Possibly the losses could have been
minimised by letting cottages with the farms and leaving the farmers
to collect rents and cope with any shortfall. Many owners, however,
in spite of the extra cost and administration, preferred to retain
direct control over their cottages because they could then vet the
occupants, prevent overcrowding and ensure that routine repairs
were carried out. It was also less intimidating to the labourer not to
be totally dependent upon the farmer for his home as well as his job.

111

The village of Lockinge on the Wantage estate in Oxfordshire
with its line of semi-detached cottages built in the 1870s.

Similar developments occurred on the Wantage estate in Oxfordshire where a banking fortune was used from the 1850s to first create
an estate out of nothing and then furnish it with all necessary
buildings and services. These included groups of new semi-detached
cottages in both the principal component villages of Ardington and
Lockinge, constructed for between £240 and £300 the pair. Most of
them had three bedrooms, two downstairs rooms, large outhouse and
garden at rents of 1s or 1s 6d per week. It was all part of Lord
Wantage's enlightened attitude to estate management, which his
widow described as being not simply a question of housing labourers
well 'but endeavouring also to render their lives less monotonous,
and to arouse their interest in matters connected with the land and
with farming. He wanted them to realise that they are not mere hired
servants, but co-operators with their landlord on a joint work in
which they have a personal stake.'[22]

112

Original premises for the co-operative stores established in the
village of Ardington, Oxfordshire, in 1888. Included in the
complex were a butchery, bakery and general store.

Theory became practice with the profit-sharing scheme introduced in the late 1880s whereby the men received a bonus payment,
proportionate to their status, from the final farm profit after all
interest charges and expenses had been deducted. The economic
climate of the time, however, was such that in some years, through no
fault of the workforce, there was little or no surplus to be divided.
Under Lord Wantage's guidance, the year 1888 saw the establishment in Ardington of village stores organised on the co-operative
system. Bread baked on the premises, general provisions and meat
were available for cash at reasonable prices while the profits, after a
deduction of 4 per cent to pay interest on capital, were subsequently
redistributed to the purchasers. There were many other manifestations of the Wantage policy: an estate savings bank; more allot-
ments; encouragement of small-holdings; and the almost constant
building – of houses, schools, parish rooms, church extensions, and

Cottages dated 1861 on the Gilston Park estate in Hertfordshire.

so on.[23] It was one of the clearest Victorian attempts to identify the welfare of the inhabitants with the well-being of the estate at large. The cost was enormous but affordable, for here were banking profits being withdrawn from the business economy and invested back into the infrastructure of the countryside.

Any traveller through modern-day rural England will find no difficulty in identifying further illustrations of the responsibility many landowners felt towards their dependent workers. Added incentive came in the shape of a continuing drift away from the land to the towns and to new overseas territories. The Agricultural Labourers' Union, whose foundation in 1872 marked a stage in the development of rural awareness, was one of the organisations that sponsored emigration when the difficulties of achieving lasting benefits through strike action were highlighted by the lock-out two years later. In theory, at least, emigration not only provided new hope for the families who went but also helped to reduce the labour supply at home and put the rural worker in a more favourable bargaining

Pair of mid nineteenth-century cottages at Forthampton,
Gloucestershire.

position. Whatever the reason, by the end of the reign labour
shortages were being commonly experienced on estates, especially as
far as the more skilled aspects of farm work were concerned. Lord
Coventry at Croome Court in Worcestershire was liberal in his
provision of excellent cottages, sick pay and pension schemes. He
still had a labour problem, however, partly, in his view, because
people did not want to live in the outlying cottages far removed from
schools and the companionship of village life and partly because there
was a marked prejudice against the physical grind of the farm
worker's routine.[24]

In spite of the good works, not forgetting that landowners were
frequently accused of pulling down more cottages than they built, the
overall picture in 1901 still pointed to a serious deficiency of adequate

housing for the rural labouring class. The low level of wages made commercial house building in the countryside the same economic non-starter that it had been all along, so the only real hope of a solution was through the intervention of public authorities. Here there had been some movement coupled with much expression of concern. The Public Health Act of 1875 went a little way towards eradicating some of the worst sanitary ills without providing any new homes to replace those condemned. Local authorities were given powers under the 1890 Housing of the Working Classes Act to build homes for those in need but at this stage few went so far as to implement them. While, therefore, the forces for a concerted attack on the housing crisis were gathering in strength, real benefits were not seen on any scale until after the First World War.

5
Livestock

A system that encouraged general land improvement, technical development and farmstead reorganisation demanded also that the accompanying livestock be adapted to their most appropriate and productive form. Animals were the living machines of the farm with levels of output and efficiency that could be manipulated and enhanced through the accumulating effects of selective breeding. By the beginning of the Victorian period these effects were already apparent for considerable developmental work had been in progress during the second half of the eighteenth century. The requirement was for stock that would mature rapidly when fed on the root crops of the arable rotation to provide abundant quantities both of the cheap, fatty meat so relished by the rising urban populations and of the rich, fertile manure that kept the land in good heart for cereals. Dual-purpose animals, such as the hardy milk and beef cattle that could also put in a day's work at the plough, were losing ground in favour of the more refined, specialist beast that had to be fed well and housed well before the desired return was obtained. Draught work demanded its own expert attention from the breeders and, appropriately enough, amongst other achievements the Victorians transformed the mongrel English cart-horse into the majestic Shire and surrounded it with all the paraphernalia of a pedigree breed.

Shorthorn cattle were early beneficiaries of the changes taking place and continued to march across England from their native pastures of the north-east at the expense of the less adaptable longhorns. In the decades either side of 1800, the work of noted breeders, among them the Colling brothers and the Booth family of Yorkshire, improved the fattening and maturing characteristics of the Shorthorn to make it an ideal occupant of the yards and stalls of arable farmsteads. Similarly with sheep, shifts in priority saw more emphasis on early maturity and mutton production than previously. By the time of his death in 1795, Robert Bakewell's New Leicester sheep, a cross nurtured at Dishley through careful selective breeding

Shire stallion Crafty William, foaled in 1896, and one of two prize stallions retained on the home farm of the Duke of Portland's Welbeck Abbey estate in Nottinghamshire to improve the quality of horses bred and used on the tenanted farms. From *Country Life,* June 1901.

over a period of years, had already made a significant impression upon English flocks and forged a path that others were to follow. Although not without its flaws, the New Leicester was a very rapid and economical weight gainer with the capability above all of transmitting chiefly its best qualities when crossed with older, unimproved breeds.

Looking back from the 1840s, early contributors to the Royal Agricultural Society's journal were struck by the degree of livestock mutation that had occurred over the preceding fifty years. In his survey of Cornwall, W. F. Karkeek described a complete alteration in the character of the native sheep largely through the efforts of a local flock-master, Mr Peters, who had begun introducing Leicester blood in 1790. As other farmers of the area followed suit, so the differences between the old and the new became pronounced:

Prize winning Leicesters bred by William Sanday of Holme Pierrepont, Nottinghamshire. At the RASE Salisbury Show of 1858, the sheep on the left was part of the first prize pen of shearling ewes, the one in the middle gained the first prize for aged rams and the one on the right the award for best shearling ram. From *The Farmer's Magazine*, August 1858.

'The saving in the cost of production through the early maturity, improvement of fleece, and of form generally, is more than 50 per cent. The old breed were kept from two years to two years and a half before sold, and the best of them did not exceed from 10 lbs to 12 lbs per quarter. They are now sold at one year and one year and a half old, averaging from 18 to 24 lbs per quarter.'[1]

In the western districts of Nottinghamshire, the indigenous breed of sheep had been 'an animal more likely to endure hardships than repay any expenditure in attempting to improve it',[2] and reflected the agricultural value of an area that at the end of the eighteenth century was described as a vast expanse of wasteland. It was upgraded, however, through the liberal application of bones and other light

119

manures so that good crops of turnips could be grown for sheep, whose manure in turn rendered the land fit for corn. Improved sheep, mostly Leicesters or Leicester-Lincolnshire crosses, could be reared in larger numbers on supplies of better-quality feed now available. Farms of 300 acres that had previously supported scarcely more than a few dozen head were by the 1840s keeping flocks of 500 or more, all of them fattening to greater weights for market. In consequence the area became noted for its breeders, including William Sanday of Holme Pierrepont, who, at the Royal Show in Salisbury in 1858, came away with all six classes of award for Leicesters and 100 sovereigns in prize money.

CATTLE

In the cattle world, it was still the Shorthorn that commanded most attention because of its ability to fatten well at an early age and produce a more uniform grade of serviceable offspring when crossed with the mediocre stock of mixed blood commonly found on many farms. The breed's prowess in the dairy suffered a corresponding decline but was considered by at least some breeders as a necessary sacrifice in the cause of developing further its weight-gaining attributes. In the middle of the century, Hall Keary, agent of the Holkham estate in Norfolk, was able to picture clearly the physical changes that had been made:

'The feeding propensities of the improved Shorthorns are well known and almost proverbial. There is something in the very touch of the flesh and silky hair of a good Durham which tells us that the animal must get fat, and in fact forms the grand characteristic of the improved over the original Shorthorns; and whoever has felt the short wiry hair and hard flesh of the old Yorkshire and Lincolnshire breed will be sensitive of the difference I have endeavoured to describe.'[3]

At three years, the animal prepared for market could weigh 6 cwt or more and if kept a little longer could be induced to increase this by another 50 per cent. There was no shortage of advice on successful and economical techniques of fattening and here the question of

The Duke of Northumberland, a Shorthorn bull bred by
Thomas Bates of Kirklevington, Cleveland. He was the winner
of the top prize of thirty sovereigns for best short-horned
bull at the English (later Royal) Agricultural Society's first
meeting at Oxford in 1839. At the age of three years eight
months, he weighed 180 stone or 22½cwt.

efficient housing, on the basis that warmth is an equivalent of food,
went hand in hand with dietary matters. Linseed cake, a by-product
of oil extraction, proved a particularly nourishing feed that resulted
also in a highly enriched manure, so that by 1847 it was reckoned that
73,000 tons of the cake were being imported annually.[4] In addition
winter rations included quantities of roots as they became available,
beginning with turnips in October and followed by swedes and
mangolds, all mixed with plenty of hay and straw chaff for bulk. The
secret was to supply the feed in its most digestible form, whether
chopped, steamed or boiled, and in fairly small but frequent amounts
to allow the beast plenty of time for ruminating.

For Shorthorns above all, the aim from the early days to fix and
pass on outstanding characteristics led to the enormous importance

The Shorthorns, Moss Rose and her daughter Young Moss
Rose, bred by Richard Stratton of Broad Hinton in Wiltshire.
Moss Rose was calved in 1838, won many prizes at West
Country shows through to 1848, and produced fifteen progeny
in all. From *The Farmer's Magazine* of January 1859.

that breeders attached to pedigree. This was why bulls of pure lineage
could fetch very high prices both before and after Colling's Comet
was sold for 1,000 guineas in 1810. The appearance in 1822 of the
Shorthorn herd book, painstakingly compiled by George Coates and
thereafter regularly updated, only increased the fascination by allowing the breed lines of individual animals to be fully assessed. To the
experienced eye, substrains of Shorthorn – which originated, for
example, from the stock of Thomas Bates at Kirklevington or of the
Booths at Warlaby – were easily identified and made the task of
unprejudiced judging in the show ring very difficult. It was, moreover, periodically a source of complaint in the middle of the century
that the pampered overfed beasts of unblemished pedigree that
collected the prizes and attracted public acclaim at the major shows
were not necessarily those that would produce progeny of the most
economic or trouble-free kind in the real world of commercial
agriculture.

One well-known Shorthorn breeder of the period never to be
diverted from the path of practicality was Richard Stratton, who,

after an initial phase at Cricklade in Wiltshire, moved in 1851 to a holding of 1,800 acres in and around Broad Hinton, a few miles south of Swindon. His reputation was built around sturdy, healthy stock that were sound in flesh but retained a good milking quality and, as he demonstrated on his own farm, an ability to perform light work in the field. A report of 1860[5] found 110 cows at Broad Hinton serving the dairy and yielding an average of about 300 gallons of milk a day in the summer, some of which was then turned into cheese at the rate of 200 lb per week. Stratton was at that time putting eight of his 2-year-old heifers to the yoke and even contemplating harnessing one of his prize bulls, Nottingham, to the mechanical butter churn instead of a horse. To achieve these all-round qualities, he had concentrated on form and appearance from whatever source it emanated, rather than a slavish adherence to pedigree, and shown a willingness to introduce new blood at intervals to avoid the weaknesses that arose from too much inbreeding.

At the root of the Broad Hinton herd was the pure Shorthorn bull Phoenix, purchased by Stratton in 1838, whose descent in the male line could be traced back to the famous Comet. Shortly before the move to Broad Hinton, Phoenix was put to a red-and-white heifer, of no known history, that had been bought at Highworth market. The result was the finely proportioned Moss Rose, a frequent prizewinner in her own right, who produced a stream of excellent calves before her death at the great age of 21. She, together with one of her daughters, Young Moss Rose, was responsible for progeny which brought top awards three times at Smithfield during the 1850s and a prize from the Paris Exhibition of 1855. International demand for Broad Hinton stock saw Moss Rose 3rd, born in 1852, auctioned in Australia for 470 guineas. Substantial sales from the herd occurred in 1867 and 1871, widely dispersing Broad Hinton blood amongst other breeders, and on Richard Stratton's death in 1878 the remainder of the herd was split between two sons, who continued the family's reputation in this field. One of them, Richard junior, argued long and hard that the dairy qualities of these cattle should be encouraged once more after so many years of neglect and succeeded in persuading the Shorthorn Society in 1901 to initiate special awards for milking characteristics.

The opposing camp was represented by breeders such as Deane Willis of Bapton Manor near Salisbury, who was an out-and-out producer of beef Shorthorns. It had not always been so, for his father

White Shorthorn ox bred by Richard Stratton in 1853. He
won many prizes including a string of top awards in
December 1856 at the Gloucester, Birmingham and Smithfield
Club Shows. In April 1857 he came away with the first prize
of forty-eight sovereigns from the Poissy Show in France
and was subsequently sold for slaughter for sixty-eight
sovereigns. From *The Farmer's Magazine* of June 1857.

had first set about building up a notable herd on the 1,000-acre estate
in the 1860s by employing good milking stock bred by Richard
Stratton. The turning-point, however, came in 1890 when the son
purchased at an average price of £100 each 32 heifers from Amos
Cruickshank's world-famous herd based at Sittyton in Aberdeen-
shire. Since the first year of Victoria's reign, Cruickshank had been
patiently developing his own distinctive strain of Shorthorn well
suited to an area that spent much of its time preparing beef for the
London market. His reputation grew dramatically after it was dis-
covered that Sittyton cattle flourished in the wide open spaces of the
Americas. When, therefore, in 1889, at the age of 82, he sold the herd,
Argentina was to be the destination. In the event, economic difficul-

The Scottish bred bull, Count Lavender, that Deane Willis took to Bapton
where it helped lay the foundations of the very successful Shorthorn herd.
Painted by James Clark in 1892.

ties prevented all but a few from travelling so the remainder were left
for resale to breeders at home. Around the heifers that Willis came
away with he built a major herd that had brought him over a
thousand awards and £8,000 in prize money by the end of the period.[6]

Two carefully chosen bulls, Captain of the Guard and Count
Lavender, were also taken to Bapton from Scotland for breeding
purposes. Amongst the champions that followed was Brave Archer, a
grandson of Count Lavender, who was sold for £1,250 to America,
while his son, C.I.V., collected most of the important titles from
shows at the beginning of the new century. The most highly ac-
claimed cow in the herd at this time was White Heather, rarely beaten
in the show ring from the Royal downwards, and managing at the
same time, despite a hectic schedule, to give birth to some fine calves.

Shorthorn progress notwithstanding, other breeds of cattle continued to occupy positions of importance through their particular
suitability to the agricultural conditions of certain areas. On the rich

grazing pastures of the western midland counties, for example, were to be found the Herefords, with their tendency to fatten well on good grass, ready for the markets of London and other major centres. Devon, notably the hilly northern district, was the home of an especially rugged and hardy breed which yet possessed a great aptitude to fatten. During the Napoleonic War period, the breed as a whole had suffered seriously from the slaughter of quality stock but thereafter it made a comeback, helped very largely by the efforts of Francis Quartly, based near South Molton, who instituted a programme of systematic improvement.

From their build and temperament, Devons were better equipped than some for work in the field. David Low in his comprehensive survey of farm stock published in 1842 wrote of them:

'They trot well in harness and will keep pace with a horse in the ordinary labours of the farm. They are largely employed throughout the county of Devon for the purposes of labour, usually four together, and mostly attached by the yoke and not by the collar. The team of labouring oxen in this beautiful county is one of the charms of the rural landscape.'[7]

Devons also found favour in other areas where a tough animal capable of existing on exposed and scant pastures was required. In Norfolk, the Holkham estate was home to a well-known herd that Thomas Coke had created. He also encouraged his tenants to keep them, and the winning Devon at the Smithfield Show of 1854 was bred by John Hudson, who farmed 1,500 acres of Holkham land at Castle Acre.

Where circumstances demanded, new breeds of cattle were developed or adopted that would fit more favourably into the new economic framework. The Aberdeen Angus, for example, was a creation of the nineteenth century. It came about because agricultural improvement in the north-east of Scotland enabled a higher calibre of beast to be kept in the harsh climate of this upland region and one that could be transported live by the new steam ships operating out of Aberdeen direct to the markets of the metropolis. Gradually, over a period of decades, skilful crossing of local strains produced a distinct type, characterised by its black colour and absence of horns, which combined a hardy constitution with a capacity for lean and tender meat of great quality packed into a

Devon cow bred by John Hudson who farmed 1,500 acres at
Castle Acre on the Holkham estate in Norfolk. In December
1854, when nearly five years old, this animal won a first
prize and silver medal at the Smithfield Club Show.
From *The Farmer's Magazine* of July, 1855.

compact frame. By the 1860s, the breed was attracting recognition
and reward at the national shows and was beginning to establish itself
in areas at home and overseas quite independent of its birthplace. In
England an Aberdeen Association was formed in 1900 and one of the
prominent members was John Cridlan of Maisemore Park in
Gloucestershire.[8] He had set about the creation of an Aberdeen
Angus herd from the early 1890s through the judicious purchase of
some of the best pure stock available in Scotland. Ten years later, his
own reputation as a breeder was such that Maisemore stock, notably
the great bull Elate, was able to successfully challenge the Scots in
competition on their home ground.

Another rising star of the Victorian period was the Channel Island
breed, which was commonly referred to initially as the Alderney
before the separate strains, chiefly from Jersey and Guernsey, were
fully recognised on the mainland. The Jersey herd book appeared in
1880 and credited the oldest English herd to Audley End in Essex,

The black bull, Elate, at Maisemore Park in Gloucestershire, home of
his breeder John Cridlan. At the beginning of the twentieth century,
Elate made a triumphal progress through the Aberdeen-Angus classes
at shows up and down the country.
From *Country Life* of July 1902.

where Lord Braybrooke had founded one in 1811. At first, import-
ations were modest for Jerseys were considered by many to be
attractive ornaments for the gentleman's estate but not suitable for
the commercial working farm. This impression changed as their
constitution became more adjusted to the harsher English climate
and their outstanding propensity for milk and butter production
came to the fore in the light of growing consumer demand. The Royal
Agricultural Society introduced classes for Channel Island cattle at
its 1844 show in Southampton and from 1871 Jerseys and Guernseys
were always divided into separate categories. A measure of the
breed's progress was that for the 1899 show at Windsor Jerseys
accounted for more than a quarter of all cattle exhibited. They
proved increasingly popular also to farmers on the continent of
Europe and in the colonies, so that on the island of Jersey itself con-

Lavanja, calved in 1891, a prodigious producer of rich
Jersey milk at Dr Watney's Buckhold estate.
From *Country Life* of November 1902.

cern was periodically expressed at the depletion of the home stock.

Amongst the leading breeders at the end of the century, Herbert
Watney of Buckhold in Berkshire was perhaps the most influential,
for his work of further reducing delicacy and improving milk yield
brought the Jersey close to its modern form. As well as paying great
attention to the housing and well-being of his herd (*see* page 77), he
instituted a precise system of record keeping to identify the highest
producers so that, through controlled breeding, he could attempt to
extend their characteristics in the progeny. His successes were
marked by numerous prizes from butter tests at agricultural shows in
the 1890s and with the award of a gold medal from the British Dairy
Farmers. The cumulative effect was that whereas in the 1840s it was
reckoned that a good Jersey cow gave about 10lb of butter weekly,
one of Watney's cows, Sharab, made 3lb 9oz under test from a single
milking and another, Lavanja, produced a maximum of 568lb in one
year and 3,500lb over the course of seven years.[9] Although the
richness and quality of Jersey milk is still highly regarded, in the late

twentieth century it is the Friesian that occupies the dominant position in English dairying through its abundant yield of milk for mass consumption. Dutch cattle have been imported for centuries, for use by dairymen and for crossing with native breeds, but not until the 1880s was there any concerted attempt to establish pure Friesian herds in England. The story of their progress belongs essentially to the post-Victorian era.

SHEEP

With sheep as with cattle, the work of improvement that had gathered momentum in the eighteenth century was continued in the nineteenth. Here the general picture is more complex for there was to begin with a much greater range of indigenous breeds that had evolved to match the specific geographical and climatic conditions of different areas. The object of any improving farmer was to rear sheep that retained the essential native traits of the district while at the same time incorporating additional desirable elements such as earlier maturity or a greater quantity of more marketable meat. In the Lake District, for example, was the Herdwick, a mountain breed with an iron constitution and a very coarse fleece surrounding mutton of the finest quality. By putting first-class Leicester or Southdown rams to Herdwick ewes it was possible to produce offspring that allied hardiness with a propensity to fatten more quickly to greater weights. Two breeds that proved very popular with overseas buyers, the huge Lincoln and the resilient Romney Marsh, were both well infused with Leicester blood by the middle of the century. Thus of the latter, T. Rowlandson could write in 1849:

'The modern Romney Marsh sheep is a very superior animal, containing a cross of about one third new Leicester blood; the wethers now arrive at market at two years old, instead of three as heretofore; the fleece and flesh continue good, and the cross has become gradually acclimatised to the bleak winds of the exposed marshes.'[10]

These qualities enabled it to populate successfully other parts of the world, from New Zealand to the Falklands, where similar conditions prevailed.

Romney Marsh sheep from David Low's *The Breeds of Domestic Animals of the British Isles*, 1842.

Improvements made upon the Southdown, a breed described at the end of the eighteenth century as small, unprepossessing and of defective carcass, were carried through not by crossing but by paying greater attention to the selection and matching of breeding stock. John Ellman of Glynde in Sussex led the way in the development of a refined version of the Southdown that was still hardy enough to thrive on the thin downland soil but also fattened earlier to a larger size and produced a highly marketable variety of lean, succulent mutton. By the end of the eighteenth century, Ellman's name had travelled the world, helped very largely by the fact that the Holkham and Bedford estates, whose annual farming festivals, or shearings, attracted many foreign visitors, both accumulated important flocks of Southdowns with Glynde derivatives. When Ellman faded from the scene in the 1820s, his mantle was taken up by Jonas Webb of Babraham in Cambridgeshire, who was to become the most renowned of all Victorian sheep breeders.

Webb began his work with Southdowns soon after setting up as a

Improved form of Lincolnshire sheep bred by John Clarke of
Long Sutton and prize winners at the 1854 Royal Show held
in Lincoln. There was some variation in sheep of this breed
according to the degree of infusion of Leicester blood, but
all were known for their large size and the quality of their
long staple wool. From *The Farmer's Magazine* of
September 1854.

farmer in his own right on the tenanted 1,000-acre Babraham Farm in
1822 at the age of 26. He chose this breed because earlier experience
gained with his father had, in his own words, convinced him

'that more mutton and wool of the best quality could be made per
acre from Southdown sheep than from any other breed, upon nine-
tenths of the arable land in this country, where sheep are regularly
folded, especially where the land is poor and the animals have far to
walk to fold.'[11]

From a foundation stock purchased at no small expense in Sussex,
the Babraham flock had attained a high degree of development by
1840 and thereafter enjoyed a position of almost unchallenged supremacy over the following twenty years.

The first awards from the Royal Agricultural Society came at

Three of Webb's Southdown rams that were exhibited at the
RASE Show in Liverpool in 1841. Two gained the first and
second prizes for shearlings while the third was judged the
best ram of any age. The Duke of Newcastle subsequently
hired one for the season at a cost of 100 guineas.
From *The Farmer's Magazine* of December 1841.

Cambridge in 1840 and the last at Canterbury in 1860, when all six
prizes offered for rams were won and the champion, Canterbury,
fetched a price of 250 guineas. In addition, there were numerous
successes at local shows around the country, at Smithfield and, on
occasion, at meetings in Ireland and Scotland. After 1840, all the
prizes gained were for young rams following Webb's refusal to enter
ewes for the show ring, where conventional practice decreed that they
should bear all the marks of overfeeding, to the detriment of their
subsequent breeding prowess, in order to be serious contenders. As a
measure of his far-reaching influence, Webb found his prize ram –
reputedly worth 500 guineas – so admired by the Emperor Napoleon
at the French International Exhibition of 1855 that he presented it to
him and later received from France in return a magnificent candelabra
of solid silver.

Breeding stock from Babraham were made commercially available

Hampshire Down ram bred by J. W. Brown of Uffcott,
Swindon, and winner of the first prize and gold medal at
the Paris Exhibition in 1856. By this date, Hampshire
Downs were highly rated in Wilts, Berks and Hants as
good wool growers and suppliers of lamb and mutton to
the London market. From *The Farmer's Magazine* of June 1860.

through the annual ram-lettings which were held on the farm every
July from the late 1820s. Consisting of an auction followed by a
splendid outdoor feast in the evening, these events rapidly grew into
great agricultural occasions, attracting anything from a few hundred
to as many as two thousand breeders, farmers and sightseers. By such
means, rams were leased for the year, at prices that could top £180 for
a really fine specimen, so that Babraham blood could work its
improving powers on some distant flock. The dissemination process
reached its climax in 1861 and 1862 when Webb, who was now 65,
decided to retire from sheep breeding and sold the entire flock of
1,404 animals, in two stages, for a total of £16,646 14s 6d. The most
valuable ram went to New Jersey in America, while other members of
the flock, male and female alike, were scattered to Australia, South
America, Canada and many of the European countries. It could as a

result be said with some authority that there would hardly be Southdowns anywhere in the world that had not received some benefit from Webb's work.

The mark of Babraham was also left on other downland breeds. An improved version of the Hampshire, for example, which became known as the Hampshire Down from the middle of the century, utilised rams from the flock in its development. The man responsible was William Humfrey, who farmed over 600 acres of strong arable land at Oak Ash, near Chaddleworth in Berkshire. His quest for a large, robust and fleshy animal that was quick to mature in the turnip fold led him in 1842 to employ the services of Webb's best Southdown rams upon his own hand-picked selection of Hampshires purchased from other breeders. Three rams were used in all, two of them proving particularly successful, at a hiring fee of 60 guineas each. Thereafter, through selective breeding within the flock, Humfrey was able to fix the type. At his death in 1868, his sheep were dispersed to other flocks, including that belonging to James Rawlence of Bulbridge near Salisbury, who, by further amalgamations, put the final touches to the breed.

PIGS

Compared with cattle and sheep, pigs were long regarded as the poor relation of the farm and undeserving of the finer aspects of the breeder's craft. In the early nineteenth century there were numerous local breeds, made even more so by much *ad hoc* intermingling of blood and infusions of Chinese and Neapolitan stock. Where pigs came to notice at all, it was often as prodigiously fat beasts that were profitable as exhibition curios but little else. For the most part, while the best cattle led pampered lives, the common pig was relegated to inadequate quarters and made do with scavenging for food as best it could. Considerable changes did come in time, however, as attention turned to the development of a more efficient animal that would deliver the kind of pork and bacon that the urban populace wanted to eat. One inevitable consequence was a narrowing of the focus onto a small number of successful breeds while the lesser varieties remained popular within closely defined areas but otherwise all but disappeared from view.

James Howard, the wealthy and talented agricultural engineer of Bedford, was also a farmer and stockbreeder of some repute, having achieved recognition in particular for his flock of Oxford Down sheep. In the early 1860s he was induced to turn his mind to pigs after reading a local report that was heavily critical of the current state of pig farming in the county. So, over the next twenty years, he studied very thoroughly the practical points of the breeding and rearing of pigs on his Clapham Park estate to the north of the town. From observation of all the major breeds, he came to the conclusion that 'none grow so rapidly or realise so much money in a given time as pure pigs of the Large White breed'.[12] He had tried out the Berkshire, the great favourite of the southern dairying districts, and praised its hardy constitution and capacity to fatten to weights of around 300 lb. The Large White, however, bred in large numbers at Clapham from stock originally purchased in its native Yorkshire, was preferred because it matured earlier and fattened to a leaner grain of meat that commanded a higher price from the bacon curers.

IMPORTS

Farmers in Denmark, too, were attracted to the Large White for the same reasons and imported many in the course of creating the important Danish bacon industry that was soon to have such an impact upon the British market. It was only one further manifestation of a trend that was arousing much wry comment in the last years of the Victorian era. The very success of breeders at home in providing quality stock to populate the farms of the world rebounded upon the domestic agricultural economy as Britain began to suck in overseas food surpluses from wherever they could be found. In spite of the arrival of faster-maturing animals and greater efficiencies provided by the new elements such as a railway network for moving stock easily from breeding to fattening grounds and then on to market, output of meat on the home front was unable to keep pace with the demands of a population growing in both numbers and purchasing power. During the 1850s and 1860s, the relatively small shortfall was made up principally through the importation of livestock and carcasses from the European continent. This in itself was not without its hazards for it was a consignment unloaded at Hull in

136

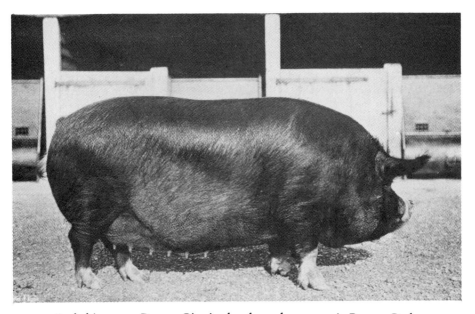

Berkshire sow, Buscot Pippin, bred on the county's Buscot Park
estate where there was also a very fine herd of Shorthorns.
The proprietor, Mr A. Henderson MP, installed many
novel features on the estate including a 1½ mile tramway to
convey crops to the farmstead and distribute manure to
the fields. From *Country Life* of September 1901.

the summer of 1865 that introduced the great cattle plague which by
the following March had been responsible, according to conservative
official estimates, for well over 140,000 deaths.

As the gap in supply widened markedly in the last quarter of the
century, so the technology of freezing meat was mastered to make its
transport across the oceans of the world a viable and profitable
activity. The first frozen cargo of sheep and lambs, over 4,000 of them,
to arrive from New Zealand was on board the *Dunedin* in 1882. A
little over a decade later, the carcasses of three million sheep were
making the same voyage every year and one hundred vessels were
employed in the trade.[13] The largest operator, Nelson Brothers,
maintained a huge five-storey cold store in Lambeth where up to
200,000 frozen sheep could be held at a time before being gradually
released upon the market when prices were favourable. In Liverpool
there were likewise very extensive facilities for transatlantic meat

The Smithfield Meat Market, opened in 1868. From *The Illustrated London News* of that year.

shipments as the United States was, by the late 1880s, sending across well in excess of a quarter of a million tons of chilled beef annually over and above the numbers of live cattle – up to 300,000 – that were also arriving.

Whatever the country of origin or the port of arrival, a large proportion of these cargoes ultimately appeared at the two principal markets in London. The Metropolitan Cattle Market at Copenhagen Fields, close by King's Cross Station, was officially opened by Prince Albert in 1855. Its 30 acres, well served by railway access, included lairages for 3,000 cattle, standings for a further 5,000 and pens for 35,000 sheep. The inadequate and overcrowded site it replaced at Smithfield subsequently became the home of a new dead-meat market, opened in 1868. With its domes and turrets, lofty avenues of cast-iron columns and massive ornamental iron gates, the structure of Smithfield remains little altered and is the finest monument in the capital to the Victorian agricultural industry. Beneath the main market hall was an underground storage and transit area extending to 5 acres and with sidings connecting directly into the main railway system. The sophisticated lines of supply and distribution, stretching over thousands of miles, were a success story and the admiration of all, except perhaps the native British farmer, who found that world competition lowered the price of meat at home by at least a quarter in the thirty years from 1870 and pushed him into a grim battle for survival.

6
Farm Equipment

Agricultural technology strode forward during the Victorian period with results that may justly be described as revolutionary. Whereas in the 1830s the dominant feature of many field tools and implements was their striking similarity to predecessors made a hundred or even two hundred years earlier, in 1900 these ties of continuity were becoming only dimly visible beneath the wealth of factory-made implements and machines now affecting almost every branch of the agricultural process. It was this that allowed farm output to be maintained even though the labour force fell in numerical strength from a peak reached at mid-century. Beneath the figures lay a fundamental shift, for, as James Caird put it, 'our agriculture is no longer influenced by considerations of the means of finding employment for surplus labour, but is now being developed on the principle of obtaining the largest produce at the least cost'.[1] Technological progress had been slowly gathering pace but it was not until the decades either side of 1850 that the mounting expertise of a maturing agricultural engineering industry met with the demands of increased productivity to set in train the mechanisation of farming methods.

The tenacity of the old against the not quite irresistible march of the new should not be underestimated for it forms one of the most colourful attributes of Victorian agriculture. Centuries of tradition and gradual evolution were not about to be pushed aside overnight and could present stubborn resistance to the adoption of new ideas, practices and equipment. The problem of how to communicate the benefits of change amongst fiercely independent and often isolated farmers could be a reinforcing factor, especially in the earlier years. Indeed, incredulity was often voiced throughout the century that on one side of a hedge the most recent improvements might be enjoying considerable success while on the other a neighbouring farmer refused to budge from outmoded principles and prejudices inherited from his forefathers. When the Smyth brothers of Peasenhall in Suffolk produced a creditable seed drill in 1807, they attempted over a number of years to overcome this resistance by sending examples out on contract hire through the southern counties so that farmers would become acquainted with the device and perhaps be enticed into purchasing one of their own. As time passed, the reflex type of opposition to change tended to fade into a more pragmatic approach, with farmers making selective forays into mechanisation while still continuing to perform other tasks in the traditional way. This commonly led to a delicate balance, a kind of mutual dependence, between both old and new on the one farm.

The technology, then, was travelling at two levels. On top was the broadening stream of science and industry, of experiment and innovation, while jogging along beneath, at a quietly slackening pace, was an alternative order representing custom, tradition and the accumulated wisdom of human experience. The first attracts so much attention that it is easy to short-change the significance of the other. Hand tools, for example, though declining in importance, were being used throughout the period. There was little the nineteenth century could contribute by way of design to the scythe, sickle or billhook, for countless generations of use had already been at work on them. Nor, simply because they were of ancient origin, were they crude: their manufacture was a highly specialised business which, since at least the eighteenth century, had concentrated itself upon major centres like Sheffield, Birmingham and, to a lesser extent, parts of the West Country. At Dunsford near Exeter, the site now occupied by the tool makers Morris & Sons has a record of activity extending back prior to the year 1821, when the surviving waterwheel that once drove the tilt hammers was installed. In works such as this, and the nearby Finch Foundry, at Sticklepath, with its equally long pedigree, skilled craftsmanship turned out agricultural tools of high renown.

What the Victorians did – to good effect – as far as the agricultural edge tool was concerned was to introduce new production processes and new types of steel to give a keener, more durable cutting edge. There were, however, other categories of hand tool, perfectly serviceable in use, that underwent no such fundamental change either in design, material or method of production. Two or three basic designs of hay rake, for example, were already long established, needed little further improvement, and could be made up without difficulty by local craftsmen wherever the raw material was available. In some districts, like the border areas between Hampshire and Berkshire, hay

Cotswold type farm wagon of the late nineteenth century with
distinctive bow raves over the rear wheels.

rakes constituted one of the staples of the woodland trades. At
Pamber End, successive generations of the Sims family made large
quantities each year from the middle of the Victorian period to well
beyond the Second World War using techniques that were considerably older. When demands for improved performance grew in
the second half of the nineteenth century, they were met not through
tinkering with the existing hand rake, for it was at the peak of its
evolutionary development, but through an entirely new implement
relying on horse rather than human power.

It was not only amongst hand tools that custom was able to prove
its stamina. The late Victorian farmer in England who took advantage of all the technological sophistication that mowing and reaping

machinery could provide was quite likely to rely still on the old-style four-wheeled wagon for removal of the harvest from the field. With its shape and form preserved by small firms of wheelwrights in each locality, the wagon possessed a regional identity that many were loath to forsake. It was an object of local pride, not to be easily subverted by experts who insisted that the lighter two-wheeled carts were more economical or by the guile of the industrial manufacturers who turned out standardised versions using much labour-saving machinery.

The inevitable, however, could not be delayed indefinitely, so that George Sturt, writing in the early 1920s of the time when he entered the family's long-established wheelwrighting business in 1884, acknowledged that 'the heyday of waggon building was over and that decline had set in from which the old craft is now well nigh dead'.[2] Compromise was necessary:

'the earlier adjustments, which in fact had given the beauty as of an organism were being neglected. Yet this neglect did not, could not, spread far. For years the old country traditions of waggon-building continued to be faithfully followed. Details which might not be cheapened still achieved the superb adjustments, and waggons grew into beauty not to please artists who gushed about them, but to satisfy carters and to suit the exigencies of field and crop and road.'[3]

A gas engine was installed in 1889, for driving turning and drilling equipment, in an attempt to improve competitive edge by applying late nineteenth-century technology to the labour-intensive practices of a craft. It helped the Sturt firm in Farnham outlast the Victorian period but in reality the end of the road for numerous businesses of this sort around the country was near at hand.

The old type of plough, a local product with accretions of local design characteristics, occupied a similar position in the agricultural world. To many a commentator searching for evidence of scientific practice it was an object of scorn, while to the farmer it was more of a loyal – if not reliable – old servant. As one exasperated reporter put it:

'There are many farmers in every district whose prejudices are so strong in favour of old customs, that the most decisive evidences of improvement will never induce them to step out of the path they have previously followed, and such will no doubt continue to plough with three horses, and even four, in length to the end of their days.'[4]

The plough after all was the most widespread and fundamental implement at the farmer's disposal and the process of ploughing not only absorbed considerable human and animal energy each year but was also a critical element in the preparation of a clean, well drained and fertile seed bed. It might therefore be expected that the improvements in design which had been emerging since the eighteenth century, to both reduce the power requirement and turn a better furrow, would be welcomed with open arms. The existence of a more efficient plough, however, was one thing; seeing it adopted to any significant degree was another.

Part of the problem early on was that designs that had evolved to work on heavy clay soils were still the basis of many ploughs, even though much lighter land was now being brought into cultivation. Furthermore, with the principal materials being wood and wrought iron, production was in the hands of carpenters and blacksmiths scattered through the countryside who were not noted for their mastery of the finer points of ploughing and might be considered reluctant to deviate from traditional practice. In 1843, Allen Ransome confirmed that ploughs continued in many districts to be the product of joint effort between two craft skills that did not always collaborate very easily. It was not difficult to see that

'the wheelwright would allow of but little interference in the course of improvement from the blacksmith and that the latter mechanic would not have his conceits thwarted by the artificer in wood; but rather that each would uphold that state of things which least interfered with the occupations of the other, and best contributed to their individual interest.'[5]

Under such an arrangement, no two ploughs were ever exactly alike for each was a one-off composed of individually formed parts. In Ransome's view, it was then a matter of luck rather than judgement whether any consistency of operation in the field would be achieved.

Ransome's low opinion was perhaps understandable, coming as he did from a family whose very name was already becoming

First floor storage areas around the covered yards at
Eastwood Manor Farm, Somerset, built in 1850.

Central section of a membership certificate for the
National Agricultural Labourers' Union issued to John Hems
of Winson, Gloucestershire, in 1876.

Leicester ram painted in 1859 by R. Whitford, one of the more
distinguished artists specialising in portraits of prize stock
in the second half of the century.

Thorney Prize Ox, bred by E. Griffin of West Ashby near
Horncastle. Winner of a Smithfield first prize, this Shorthorn
was sold for £65 at Christmas 1858, aged four years and five
months, and weighing 128 stone.
(Lithograph from a painting by James Clark.)

The Prize Shorthorn at the Chichester Show of 1856,
painted for its proud owner by William Smith.

OLD ENGLISH BREED.

Old English sow from David Low's
The Breeds of the Domestic Animals of the British Islands, 1842.

Nineteenth-century village forge at Bramley, Hampshire

The Agricultural Machinery Hall of the
Great Exhibition of 1851.

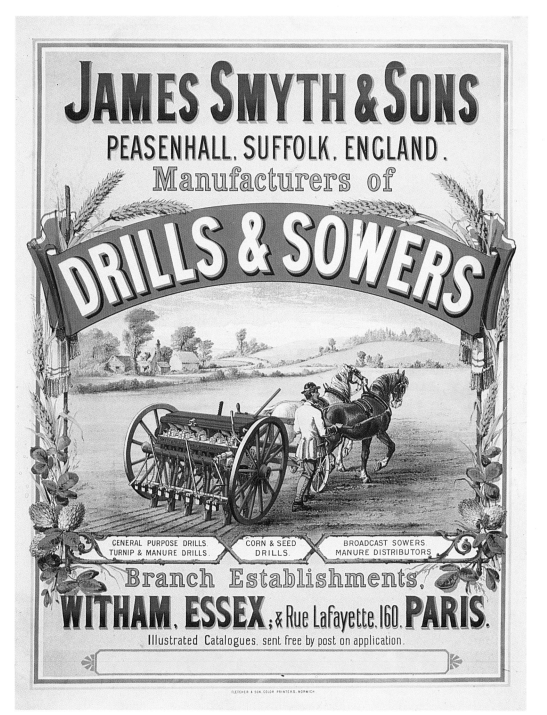

Advertising poster of the 1890s.

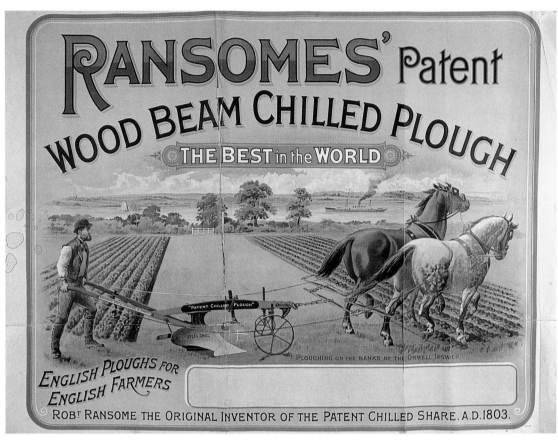

Advertising poster of the 1890s.

Single cylinder horizontal steam engine by Ransomes of
Ipswich at the works yard of the Englefield estate in
Berkshire, where it was used principally to drive equipment
in the sawmill. It was installed in 1900, replacing an
earlier engine, and although now out of service is
maintained in running order by enthusiasts.

Sack hoist mechanism at the top of the watermill
on Heydon Mill Farm, near Aylesbury in Buckinghamshire,
built in the 1830s.

Victorian agricultural technology continues to find admirers
at the steam rallies that are now a regular feature
of the countryside in summer.

Horse ploughing, combining the skills of the breeder, the
agricultural engineer and the ploughman, reached its apogee
in the late Victorian period and is kept alive today
principally through demonstrations and competitions.

synonymous with the new world of agricultural engineering. Even he was prepared to admit that tolerably good ploughs could result when they were built by one skilled man alone. Others, perhaps not so burdened by vested interest, were prepared to go much further. William Dickinson, in a mid-century review of Cumberland farming, believed that

'almost every parish has its ploughmaker, who watches the agricultural exhibitions, ferrets out and compares the alterations and improvements, adopts and applies such as his judgement or fancy approves, and has them tested by some favourite ploughman before being submitted to public scrutiny. Most of these home-made ploughs are simple and light in construction, yet strong enough for the stiff and stony soils they encounter; are neatly finished and fit to compete in the hands of a Cumberland plough-man, in any trial field in the Kingdom.'[6]

The real position overall was probably somewhere between these two extremes. Locally made ploughs included the good along with the bad but both were being progressively edged out by the more standardised products of bigger firms.

The hitherto central influence of the rural smiths and 'hedgerow carpenters' thus went into steady decline as the nineteenth century unfolded. It was a slow process because, although less involved in the actual production of equipment, they remained in demand for repair and servicing work and for the supply of a multitude of fittings in wood and iron around the farm. The well organised agricultural estate was not complete without its complex of shops equipped with extensive machinery and skilled workers capable of meeting the needs of the dependent farms, while larger holdings often incorporated their own maintenance facilities within the farmstead layout. For the rest, few villages were without a general-purpose forge where the farmer went not only to shoe the horses but also perhaps to replace the iron tyre of a wheel or the tines of a harrow.

In addition to the individual one-off construction of implements in the small craft workshop came their assembly from standardised parts in the engineering works, some of which were employing well over a thousand men by 1900. The movement had begun a century earlier when the pressure of war with Napoleon had raised the

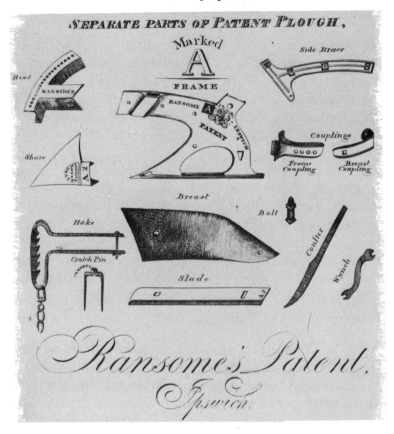

Leaflet issued to purchasers of Ransomes ploughs in the 1830s
detailing by name the separate iron parts of the A type
Patent Plough. This was to avoid confusion arising from
terminology when ordering spare or replacement parts.

domestic demand for more effective, labour-efficient equipment and
stimulated the rapid expansion of a number of specialist producer
firms. One of these, established by Robert Ransome in the 1780s,
achieved extra prominence through a system of plough manufacture
that set the standard for future progress. Ransome made two key
breakthroughs. First, he used tempering and chilling techniques to
overcome the inherent softness of cast iron and make it more suitable
for use in the production of plough shares. The great advantage of the
casting process was that any number of these hardened ploughshares,
each one identical with the next, could be turned out for distribution
through a dealer network that Ransome was beginning to create
throughout East Anglia even before 1800. Not only were the shares

Small iron foundry, established in 1809, in the Norfolk village
of Great Walsingham. It was owned by the Cornish family in
the nineteenth century and counted amongst its diverse
product line a number of agricultural implements, including
ploughs, for the immediate locality.

good in themselves but they were cheaper than the wrought-iron
counterpart, did not have to be regularly sharpened and were very
easily replaced, when necessary, with others exactly similar. Frequent
time-consuming trips to the blacksmith for repair and resetting of
shares, hitherto a tiresome feature of ploughing, could now be
avoided.

Ransome's second major contribution came in 1808 with the
concept of the interchangeable component. By standardising a basic
range of plough bodies, still of wood at this stage, and producing a
variety of components in both cast and wrought iron to bolt on to
them, he was able to extend the selection of designs available with
little additional effort. From different permutations of these parts he
could assemble ploughs that approximated in appearance and performance to the regional variations in use around the country. For

the first time, the potential then existed for the creation of a national market for implements provided that the necessary sales and distribution networks could be organised. This came later but the ground was at least being prepared for the emergence of a fully fledged agricultural engineering industry in the Victorian era.

Apart from the Ransome operation in Ipswich, there were other small businesses that flourished under the special conditions of the Napoleonic War period and made the vital cross-over from the status of general smiths or ironfounders to implement manufacturers of regional importance. Firms such as Garrett of Leiston in Suffolk, Burrell of Thetford, Hornsby of Grantham and Howard of Bedford were all in being and represented the seed from which later giants of the industry would grow. Collectively, they were making steady progress on the quality of farm equipment available. Take-up of the threshing machine, first introduced in the 1780s, was encouraging and development work was proceeding, while the seed drill, as already mentioned, had reached a practical form and now needed to tackle the problem of customer resistance. For a host of other implements, from harrows to field rolls, horsehoes to chaff cutters, it was a case of firming up the designs, making use of iron where feasible and generally looking more closely at efficiency and durability.

THE ROYAL AGRICULTURAL SOCIETY

A hiatus followed the outbreak of peace in 1815 as agriculture lurched from its wartime boom into recession. Further developments went into cold storage and the implement firms were obliged to diversify into other branches of engineering while waiting for the good times to return. Things did begin to improve slowly in the first decade of Victoria's reign so that demands for farm equipment were revived. At this point there appeared a new organisation to take the place of the now defunct Board of Agriculture. It was to play a vital role in the encouragement and diffusion of agricultural technology over the course of the century. The English Agricultural Society was founded in 1838 with Earl Spencer as its first president, and was renamed the Royal Agricultural Society when Victoria granted a charter and extended her patronage in March 1840. Under Earl Spencer's guidance, the Society adopted the motto 'Practice with Science', signifying its dedication to the pursuit of agricultural improvement with all the committed faith in the power of progress that the Victorian age could muster.

The presentation of farming equipment was, from the beginning, close to the heart of the Society's annual peripatetic show. At the first gathering in Oxford in 1839, visited by 20,000 people, there were nineteen exhibitors, of whom Ransome was the most prominent, having sent 6 tons of machinery and implements down by wagon from Ipswich. Two years later in Liverpool, both the number of contributing manufacturers and the quality of their products were thought to have increased considerably, leaving Josiah Parkes and his fellow judges in no doubt as to the positive effects of the Society's encouragement.

'This vast stride in the mechanics of agriculture, made within so short a period, has doubtless arisen from the congregating together of agriculturists and mechanicians from all parts of the empire; and a still higher perfection in machinery may be confidently anticipated from the opportunity offered, under the auspices of the Society, of periodically contrasting and estimating the merits of varied implements used for similar purposes in different localities and soils.'[7]

When the show returned to Oxford in 1870, having during the intervening years travelled to sites as far apart as Lewes, Lincoln, Newcastle, and Plymouth, the tally of exhibitors passed the 350 mark. There was no doubting its value as a shop window for agricultural engineering that enabled manufacturers to build up national markets which, with the spread of the railway system and establishment of local agencies, could now be served satisfactorily. Furthermore, impetus could be maintained at the regional and district level through a host of local agricultural associations, many of them holding shows of their own, which sprang into existence in the Victorian period and could be numbered in their hundreds by mid-century.

The competitive flavour produced at the Royal by the system of implement trials and award of prizes was an added spice of great interest to the spectators but periodically a source of discontent among some at least of the manufacturers, who were less convinced of its real benefits in terms of technological improvement. The earliest

Employees of the Reading Ironworks with the portable steam
engine of eight nominal horse power that received favourable
comment at the 1872 RASE Show in Cardiff, but under trial
was narrowly beaten into second place by Clayton &
Shuttleworth of Lincoln.

prizes were given for little more than physical appearance but during
the 1840s the manner of subjecting similar categories of equipment to
assessment in the field or show yard slowly evolved. In 1848, the
absence of objective, scientific standards against which to measure
the worth of implements was overcome when Charles Amos, consulting engineer to the Society, ensured that the dynamometer, a refined
version of the spring device first introduced in 1797 to test the
draught of ploughs, should now be applied to all classes of equipment
where appropriate. This allowed the ratio of power input to work
output to be recorded as a useful comparative guide to performance.
Until 1855, the judges tested all the machines exhibited but so

colossal did this task become that periodic trials for the different categories were then introduced first on a three-year and subsequently, in 1873, on a nine-year cycle.

The Society pointed to the sometimes very dramatic increases in efficiency that occurred over time to demonstrate the salutary effects engendered by the spirit of competition. So, for example, the $11\frac{1}{2}$lb of coal burnt per horsepower per hour by the prize winning steam engine of 1849 had been reduced to $4\frac{1}{3}$lb in 1853, $2\frac{3}{4}$lb in 1872 and $1\frac{4}{5}$lb in 1887.[8] For the most part, however, these were specially tuned competition models – the contemporary term was 'racers' – that were of little practical utility on the farm. Other factors, such as the introduction of the compound engine in 1879, offered more realistic prospects of fuel savings. Nevertheless, it seemed fair to take some credit for a general raising of standards by allowing the smaller firms the opportunity to match their innovative skills against those of the engineering giants. None of this dispelled the manufacturers' recurring criticism that trials judges were too easily sidetracked by novelty alone and awarded prizes on the evidence of an exceptional, one-off performance in what were necessarily artificial conditions rather than on what was likely to give the most economical and reliable service in the hands of the agricultural labourer. These feelings were fuelled by a certain amount of commercial nervousness over the years, for a firm that had been successful on the trial ground on previous occasions, and had built up a lucrative reputation partly as a result, might well be loath to risk all again for fear of losing out to a rival. Occasionally, the misgivings blew up into outright hostility and resulted in the non-appearance of many of the leading names at the Canterbury Show of 1860 and in a joint refusal to take part in the steam engine trials at Newcastle in 1887.

In spite of the love-hate relationship, the Royal Shows clearly charted the progress of technological change. They began at a time when the seed drill was going through a cycle of rapid development, with more and more makers appearing on the scene each with their own refinements to put forward. Still a novelty in 1839, the number exhibited at the Derby Show of 1843 rose to sixty-one and by now the prime features of the standard cup feed drill were so well established as to necessitate little further innovative work of significance over the rest of the century. The impetus then passed to drainage, reflecting the general enthusiasm of the day and the financial assistance

Farm Equipment

JAMES SMYTH & SONS'

PATENT LEVER CORN DRILLS,

FOR LIGHT SOILS.

IN order that the above Drills may be exactly suitable for light soils they are constructed throughout lighter and of smaller dimensions than our common Corn Drills (shown on pages 3 to 5), and in consequence of such construction they are never furnished with Press Irons.

They are made with J. S. & SONS' Patent Cogging Apparatus, and can also be supplied with any of the extras enumerated below.

PRICES.

No.				£	s.	d.
37.	New Drill with 7 Rows and 1 Corn Barrel			19	15	0
38.	,,	8	,, ,,	20	15	0
39.	,,	9	,, ,,	22	5	0
40.	,,	10	,, ,,	23	10	0

N.B.—The above prices are calculated at 6 inches from Row to Row. Wider distances are subject to an extra charge.

The following **EXTRAS** may be had with the above Drills.

	£	s.	d.
Improved Fore-Carriage Steerage (not exceeding 5 ft. in width) ...	4	5	0
Hind Swing Steerage	2	10	0
Wrought Iron Stalks to Coulters, extra each	0	1	3
Wrought Iron Levers instead of Wood	0	2	6
Double Cup, arrangement for drilling seeds with the Corn Barrel, each Drill	0	10	0
Separate Seed Barrels, per wheel, including spindle	0	5	0

From the Smyth catalogue of 1873.

WELLER'S PATENT DRAIN PIPE AND TILE MACHINE.

Early drainage tile machine, illustrated on a mid nineteenth-
century poster of Richard Garrett & Sons of Leiston
in Suffolk.

available for schemes through governmental and other agencies. Two tilemaking machines, a new invention without which it would have scarcely been possible to undertake large-scale drainage works at an economic cost, were shown in 1843 and thirty-four at York in 1848. Thereafter it was for some years the portable steam engine and threshing machine that caught most attention as competing firms struggled with one another to perfect the equipment now that the practice of rick-side threshing by steam in the open air had been accepted.

STEAM CULTIVATION

Steam, the ubiquitous symbol of Victorian industry, was considered by many at the time to hold the key to a new age of mechanised agriculture. When appropriate, the stationary engine could be installed at the farmstead and so arranged as to power a number of separate machines in the manner of a small factory. Of perhaps greater potential, however, was the movable engine. Not only could it reduce the cartage of materials and allow work to take place in the most convenient location, it also held out the prospect of cultivation

A Ransomes portable steam engine and threshing machine
at work in 1862.

through mechanical means. Threshing was the principal processing
operation on the farm and, beginning with the appearance of Ransome's portable steam engine and threshing machine at the 1841
show, technical progress was rapid, especially after the trials held
later in the decade where the question of mechanical efficiency came
under close scrutiny. In 1848, the subsequent grain-dressing process
was successfully incorporated by the Thetford-based firm of Charles
Burrell and over the rest of the century most additional improvement
work was centred on these combined threshing and dressing machines
which in a single operation gave the farmer a finished grain sample
ready for market. The economies now possible over laborious hand-
powered methods did not need emphasising but the cost of purchasing the equipment and the problems of maintaining it adequately
would have deterred many had it not been for the emergence of
contract hirers willing to send out threshing sets, with their experienced operators, on a working progress from farm to farm. For
obvious reasons, these firms concentrated mainly on self-propelled –

Steam ploughing system manufactured by Howard of Bedford
from the late 1850s and based on a type devised by William
Smith, a Buckinghamshire farmer, in 1855. The engine drove
each cable drum alternately to wind the implement back and
forth across the field. From the Howard catalogue of 1861.

or traction – engines, which by the 1860s were being built in large
numbers.

The application of steam to land cultivation was a challenge taken
up with enthusiasm by an agricultural engineering industry growing
in both stature and confidence from the mid-point of the century.
Logistically, the innate difficulties of operating steam engines in the
field produced a number of solutions – most, though not all, using
cables to wind implements back and forth rather than direct traction.
The basic principles were established quite early on so that the judges
at the Royal Show of 1856 were sufficiently optimistic to declare:

'There seems now no reason to doubt that the cultivation of land by
the mighty agency of steam will be accomplished, that what has
hitherto been regarded as the fond dream of theorists will become a
reality and that agriculture will be rescued from the reproach that it
has been unable to use in its daily operations an agency which has
been such an element of power and prosperity to all other industries.'[9]

At this stage, the roundabout system was predominant, with its relay of cable from the implement around or across the field, assisted by anchored pulleys, to an engine and winding drum parked on the edge. While versions of this arrangement remained available throughout the century, by 1862 practical mastery of the traction engine had led to an alternative that utilised two engines slowly progressing down opposite sides of the field winding the implement to and fro between them.

Some landlords, such as the Earl of Ducie at Sarsden in Oxfordshire, maintained a set of tackle for the use of their tenants, for generally only the bigger farmers could afford to invest in steam-plough equipment of their own, especially as the more expensive double-engine system, for reasons of convenience and ease of working, emerged as the most viable. The operational side, therefore, was dominated by contractors, some of whom rapidly generated very large enterprises: one firm in the north-east of England was reported in 1871 as having a capital of £42,000, much of it accounted for by the twenty double engine sets with which about 60,000 acres were worked each year.[10] A more sober view of the subject was provided by the Royal Agricultural Society's exhaustive report on steam cultivation published in 1867. The investigators visited the earliest of the firms, the West Riding Steam Ploughing, Cultivating & Threshing Company, which had been founded in Wakefield in 1862, with a paid-up share capital of £3,300. Two sets of double-engine tackle were in use – both built by John Fowler of Leeds, the premier manufacturer in this field – and for tillage produced earnings before costs of about £700 per year. Although the company was profitable, it experienced great difficulty in making the best of the equipment because many of the fields were too small – less than 10 acres at times – access was difficult, lanes were narrow and in the years before 1865 there were legal restrictions on the movement of engines on the road during daylight hours. So in 1864 a little over 1,400 acres was tilled, but this was divided among thirty-eight different farms and the engines had had to expend considerable time and money in travelling a total of 318 miles between jobs.[11]

Steam cultivation did not suit everyone but for some farmers in some areas it could bring real benefits. Whether the land was ploughed or stirred by a cultivator, the power of steam made possible a deeper level of tillage which, especially on the heavier soils,

FOWLER'S STEAM PLOUGH.

ENGINE AND WINDLASS.

PLOUGH.

ANCHOR.

[See following pages.

Early version of steam cultivating equipment developed by
John Fowler of Leeds in the mid 1850s. It utilised a four-
furrow balance plough which was drawn to and fro between
the engine and double windlass on one side of the field
and a mobile pulley carriage anchored on the other.

157

Ploughing engines in the yard of Eddison & Allen, steam cultivating contractors of Dorchester, in 1885. These engines have winding drums mounted beneath their boilers and worked in pairs, one on either side of the field.

improved drainage and aeration to bring a pay-off in more vigorous plant growth. Under favourable circumstances, it was cheaper and quicker than conventional methods so that vital tillage operations could be completed promptly, even in very busy periods of the farming year, to take full advantage of seasonal conditions. Steam could also be used with good effect to pull the mole drainer through the soil and create a simple but efficient means of land drainage. In the wide open spaces of eastern England, and other areas where the terrain was suitable, farms and farm practices could be more easily adapted to meet the optimum working requirements of these massive steam engines. Elsewhere, in those districts where fields were not so level, accessible or regular in form, and where the average size was well under the 30 or 40 acres considered desirable, it was much more difficult to achieve any significant penetration. Consequently, while being a technological success story, steam cultivation never really fulfilled in England all its early expectations or made the far-reaching impact that so many had expected.

REAPING MACHINES

A more fundamental breakthrough occurred in the harvest field. Experimentation with prototype reaping machines was widespread in the first half of the century and in Scotland the Reverend Patrick Bell had by the late 1820s produced a workable device which attracted a lively interest but was not built in any significant numbers until a later date. The pace of change accelerated markedly following the appearance of two American machines, the McCormick and the Hussey, at the Great Exhibition of 1851. Prompted by the obstacle that labour shortages presented to the further expansion of American agriculture, both of these reapers had been under active development for nearly twenty years and had now reached a stage of operational effectiveness, though some adjustments were necessary to allow them to perform well in British conditions. McCormick's machine was pulled by two horses and worked by two men, one to drive and the other to stand at the rear and rake the cut crop off the platform. Under trial in England in 1851, its maximum output of over 15 acres in a day of 10 hours offered exactly those prospects of savings in time and money likely to appeal to British farmers, who were finding the peak labour demands of harvest an increasingly expensive and difficult burden. As a result demand was high, so a number of domestic manufacturers very quickly stepped in to produce their own versions of the American originals and Bell's machine enjoyed a new lease of life at the hands of the Yorkshire-based firm of Crosskill.

Ten years after the Great Exhibition, reapers at work in this country were numbered in their thousands. With such a buoyant market and so many names competing for a share, technical refinements to improve lightness of draught, reliability and performance came thick and fast. In the early 1860s, mechanical means of delivering the cut crop to the side appeared and were incorporated into machines, such as the self-raking reaper built by Samuelson of Banbury, in a form that remained substantially the same over the rest of the century. Towards the end of the 1870s, and again with American manufacturers making the early running, attention turned towards the next logical labour-saving step, the self-binding reaper. The successful development of an automatic knotting mechanism for

159

The reaping machine by Cyrus McCormick of Virginia which
attracted such attention at the Great Exhibition in 1851. The
crop was swept onto the knives by the revolving creel and
then raked off to the side by a man carried at the back.

the sheaves, using wire at first but soon switching to twine, led to a
highly sophisticated machine that only the bigger and more specialist
firms could hope to build in large numbers at a price to match the
American imports. By the end of the Victorian period, reapers and
binders were between them at work on the great majority of corn
harvested in Britain. This perhaps more than anything else confirmed
the arrival of mechanised agriculture.

Across the remainder of the farming spectrum, no area was left
entirely untouched by the flair and enterprise of the agricultural
engineer. Dairying, for example, could number the cream separator
among its more spectacular developments. This first appeared, in its
Swedish form manufactured by de Laval, at the Royal Show of 1879
and its ability to divide cream from milk mechanically, using centrifugal force, marked the beginning of the end for the laborious use in
the dairy of separating pans. British firms such as Lister of Dursley
and the Dairy Supply Company soon joined in with their own
versions but the German and Scandinavian influence in this whole
sector remained very strong. The problems associated with mechan-
ising the milking parlour were less easy to overcome in spite of many
efforts in the second half of the century. A practical solution was
found right at the end of the period in the pulsating vacuum pump,

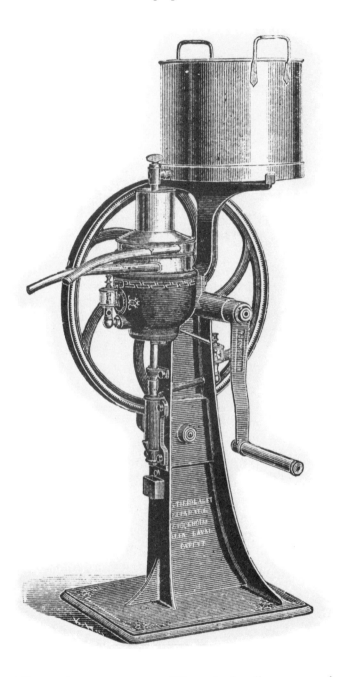

The Alfa Laval cream separator. When the handle was turned, milk in the central compartment was spun at high speed to divide off the lighter cream by centrifugal force. Cream and skimmed milk then ran out through the separate tubes shown.

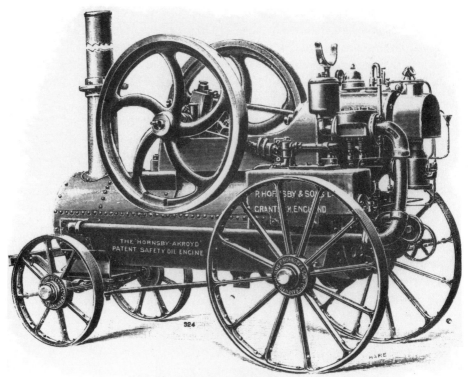

THE HORNSBY-AKROYD PORTABLE OIL ENGINE.

Hornsby-Akroyd portable oil engine. Hornsbys of Grantham
started building oil engines in 1892, having purchased the
rights from the engine's designer, Akroyd Stuart.

which painlessly and hygienically imitated the sucking of a calf, but
machine milking did not make many inroads until a later date.

THE INTERNAL COMBUSTION ENGINE

Another portent for the future was the growing interest being shown
during the 1890s in the internal combustion engine, fired by gas or
oil, for driving farm processing machinery, from the thresher at one
end of the scale down to the small chaff cutters and root slicers at the
other. For the common run of intermittent operations in the barn or

162

dairy, it scored over the steam engine in that it could be started and stopped very easily without wastage of time or fuel. When working in the field, the troublesome ferrying of coal and water was no longer necessary. The judges at the Royal Show in Cardiff in the final year of the reign reported:

'Perhaps the most striking feature of the exhibition was the number and excellence of the oil engines that were attracted by the prizes offered by the Society. In simplicity of construction, ease of manipulation, and economy of working, these machines have made great strides towards perfection, and appear to be running the rival steam engine a close race for supremacy; so that one could not help wishing that it had been possible to chronicle some attempt towards the development of this form of motor power for agricultural purposes in the field. There appear to be many agricultural operations to which a light but powerful motor, obtainable at a reasonable cost may be applied, with the advantage of greater economy and rapidity over horse power.'[12]

They did not have to wait long for in Biggleswade Dan Albone's Ivel tractor was already in the prototype stage and two years later was demonstrated to the Society both pulling a three-furrow plough and driving stationary machinery from a side pulley-wheel. With it, the seed of a new agricultural age was sown.

7
The Agricultural Engineers

Typically, the successful Victorian agricultural engineer was a small-town celebrity ruling with paternal benevolence over the local populace, a sizeable proportion of which was in his employ. As perhaps a second- or third-generation member of a family business that had risen from small beginnings, he now commanded the same kind of respect in this social setting as a landed proprietor did in his. Deservedly so, for it was the family name on ploughs, steam engines or seed drills that pushed an often otherwise little-known provincial or rural backwater into agricultural prominence not only nationally but, for some, internationally as well. Great personal reputations were built on an ability to transpose contemporary advances in mechanics into a farming context, to look at the farmers' needs in terms of output and efficiency and then meet them with competitively priced products using whatever means of industrial manufacture were appropriate. These were the hands and minds driving the nineteenth-century revolution in agricultural technology.

From its formative period in the Napoleonic War era, when some of the most important names first came to public notice, the new agricultural engineering industry marked time for a quarter of a century before moving ahead again during the 1840s. It is difficult to be numerically precise about the firms involved, but certainly at the Great Exhibition of 1851 three hundred separate makers of agricultural equipment were represented and twenty years later the likely size of the industry as a whole was double this figure. Mere numbers, however, mask the wide divergence in scale between the individual firms. At one end were the smaller village concerns, merely a step or two above the level of the craft workshop, with only a very limited and unsophisticated product range of their own for a predominantly local clientele and with the remainder of their business taken up with the sale and repair of equipment made by others. The other end was occupied by the top tier of major manufacturers having perhaps a thousand or more employees each in the last quarter of the century,

Chandler's patent liquid manure drill as manufactured by
R. & J. Reeves of Bratton. From the catalogue of 1863.

extensive catalogues displaying most types of farm equipment and an impressive network of agents and suppliers stretching across the country and around the world.

R. & J. REEVES OF BRATTON

Between these two extremes was a large group of middle-order firms that sprang from a solid local base and exerted a predominantly regional influence, while at the same time developing a small but useful trade much further afield. In this category was the family concern of R. & J. Reeves, centred on the Wiltshire village of Bratton, nestling beneath the Downs on the road from Devizes to Westbury. Its roots extended back to 1764, when Robert Reeves was apprenticed to the local blacksmith, Thomas Pepler, subsequently married his employer's daughter and ultimately was left in sole command of the business.[1] He in turn was succeeded by a son, Thomas, who in 1808 moved the firm to a site close to the Baptist church that was to remain its home for the next 162 years. At this stage, most of the work was of a general nature but by at least the second decade of the century agricultural implements, notably ploughs, were beginning to feature more prominently. As the years passed, so the range was broadened to include scarifiers, horsehoes, and, a sure sign of growing expertise, corn drills.

It was frequently the case with these firms that success in one class of implements or machine brought them wider acknowledgement and raised their entire operation to a higher plane. For Reeves, the breakthrough came in the form of the liquid manure drill. This was the brainchild of Thomas Chandler, an enterprising farmer from Heytesbury in Wiltshire, who patented the device in 1847 and came to an arrangement with Reeves over its manufacture and distribution. The problem Chandler had set out to overcome concerned the summer sowing of turnips and the difficulty in seeing the young plants off to a good start during this dry period before the onset of the autumn rains. On the new drill, therefore, a water container was mounted beneath the seed box and supplied sufficient liquid into the chutes to prompt a quick and healthy germination. Chandler's own recommendation was a rate of about 300 gallons of water to the acre, at which level it was still possible for a one-horse drill to cover six or seven acres a day. Furthermore, the water was an ideal medium for distributing in solution the manures, such as guano and superphosphate, that were coming into more general use. In this respect, the manure drill proved to be applicable to corn as well as all types of root crops and a promising potential opened up before it.

Between them, Reeves and Chandler lost no time in bringing the drill to the attention of the farming public. A medal was awarded at the York meeting of the Royal Agricultural Society in 1848 and further favourable comment came at the Exeter Show of 1850 and the Great Exhibition the following year. In addition, the firm returned from the Crystal Palace with a prize medal for a related piece of equipment, a liquid manure distributor, which was also designed by Chandler. This was essentially a water cart adapted, with a series of revolving buckets inside driven from the main axle, to make it capable of depositing a regular flow of anything from thin solutions of artificial manure to quite thick farmyard sludge. These successes were quickly reflected in lively sales and, adopting the normal marketing conventions of the day, Reeves in 1853 produced a small drill and distributor catalogue packed with details of awards gained and the text of many testimonials gathered from satisfied customers.

Thomas Reeves had died in 1849 but the business continued to grow and prosper under the two sons, Robert and John, who then took command. Building upon the experience and reputation already gained, they extended the range of drills and distributors, using ideas and designs that originated in the Bratton works itself. So, for example, while Chandler's liquid manure drill remained in the catalogue, by 1859 an improved version employing Reeves's patent refinements was also available. It arose from the introduction by factory methods of a more finely ground artificial manure which, in solution, could be run off freely from the bottom of the distributor box rather than having to be lifted out by revolving buckets. As the new powdered forms of superphosphate and guano could be distributed in their dry state, and as difficulties with water supply made the liquid drill impractical on some farms, Reeves devised the Economical Wiltshire Drill to deliver seed and pure manure down separate tubes in one operation. This was first publicly exhibited in 1857 and received a silver medal at the Royal Agricultural Society's Salisbury Show in that year. A small two-row adaptation, equipped with concave rollers to form a ridge onto which turnips, mangolds or carrots were then sown, won the second prize at the Leeds Show of 1861, as did the firm's conventional lever-type corn drill, which had been undergoing steady improvement for thirty years.

In this most important branch of its manufacturing activity, Reeves had by the early 1860s established its credentials and the product range that would see it through the rest of the century. The catalogue of December 1900 contained only slightly altered versions of the same drills, even Chandler's water drill which had first appeared over fifty years earlier. Production records show that the total number of drills and distributors of all types made up to this date was just short of 6,000.[2] Destinations included all parts of the country, with a strong bias to Wiltshire and neighbouring counties, and there was a very small export trade as well, helped in the early days by successful exhibits at such events as the German Farmers' and Foresters' Show of 1861 and the French International Exhibition in Lille, 1863. The rest of the material in Reeves's own name remained

Demonstrating a late nineteenth-century hand-cranked sheep
shearing machine patented by R. & J. Reeves.

tied primarily to the specific requirements of the local market and
included light-land ploughs, water carts and shepherds' huts. More
specialised equipment was brought in from other manufacturers. The
catalogues of the 1850s were filled out with implements and machines
made by firms like Howard, Nicholson, Bentall and Ransome, while
later catalogues simply stated that Reeves could supply any need
from steam engines and threshing machines to wagons, reapers and
cheese presses.

   The essence of R. & J. Reeves, and many other small to medium-
sized businesses in the same mould, was that it was very firmly rooted
in the local agricultural community, grew steadily but unspectacu-
larly, in this case from a workforce of 14 to 55 twenty years later, and
won wider acclaim through developing an expertise in a narrowly
defined sector of the industry. Reeves maintained the formula in the
twentieth century although it was without doubt the agency rather
than the manufacturing side of the business that became the more

important. Even so, a total of 276 drills were made after the Second World War and most of them were little different from their Victorian counterparts apart from the requirements imposed by tractor haulage. The last one appeared in 1960, ten years before the final closure of the firm.

R. HUNT OF EARLS COLNE

Operating at a rather higher level, but still bearing many similar characteristics, was the firm founded originally by Robert Hunt, a millwright, in the small Essex village of Earls Colne on the road between Colchester and Halstead. As the firm grew so, in a farming district such as this, the production of agricultural equipment began to figure more prominently amongst the daily round of routine wood and metal work. At Hunt's death in 1855, his three sons, Thomas, Robert and Reuben, were left in control of a business that made ploughs, small barn equipment and a threshing machine or two for the immediate locality. A rather more concerted drive for expansion became evident from 1867, the year that Reuben Hunt, following the death of his two brothers and still only in his early thirties, became sole proprietor. Sales figures[3] which had been static over the preceding few years soon began an upturn as Hunt concentrated on building a reputation in such lines as chaff cutters, root pulpers and other feed-processing machinery for operation by hand or horse power. Crucially, at the end of 1871 Hunt bought from Ransomes of Ipswich the manufacturing rights to its very successful range of equipment in this category for the very reasonable sum of £2,000.

For its part, Ransomes had moved into other sectors, particularly the production of steam engines and threshing machines, to the point where some slimming down of product lines was necessary for the firm to operate effectively in what had become a highly competitive market. It was therefore happy to unload a secondary part of its catalogue onto a smaller neighbour, from whom there was no serious commercial threat, especially as a distant relation of Reuben Hunt was a member of the Ransomes board. The equipment concerned included turnip cutters, cake breakers, oat and bean mills, some bearing the patent of an employee, Arthur Biddell, and generally considered to be amongst the best available. In addition to acquiring

Inside the foundry of Hunt's Atlas Works at the beginning of
the twentieth century.

the patterns and some of the machinery for making these items, Hunt
also gained access to the goodwill and the markets that Ransomes had
built up both at home and abroad. Using the established dealer
network, sales opportunities opened up in Western Europe and in
Russia, where state encouragement of agriculture had substantially
increased the volume of equipment imported. Trade with the colonies, especially Australia, Southern Africa and India, also began to
figure, accounting for about a quarter of all foreign sales by the end of
the 1870s, while other countries such as Egypt and some South
American states were also customers of significance. Foreign conditions necessitated certain adjustments to products to allow, for
example, a horse gear to be operated satisfactorily by the slower pace
of a bullock.

By these means, Hunt's annual sales, which had been at the £1,000
level in the 1850s, more than doubled in the last quarter of the
century from under £30,000 to over £64,000 with up to 20 per cent of

Machinery warehouse at the Atlas Works showing chaff cutters, of the type that could be driven by a simple horse gear or small steam engine, lined up and awaiting dispatch.

the total in some years going for export. At this stage, however, the business was not exclusively agricultural for in 1886 the manufacture of pulleys and shafting for power transmission in general industry was taken up and gradually absorbed an increasing share of the output. Physical expansion was a necessary part of commercial growth and a new base in Earls Colne, to be known as the Atlas Works, was taken over in 1870. Today, progressive development of the 10-acre site can be clearly traced through a line of engineering shops bearing dates that follow in sequence through the 1870s. Part of the finance for this work came from a local businessman, James Tawell, who injected £7,000 into the business from 1872 in return for a partnership with Hunt that lasted for fourteen years. Earls Colne itself grew from a village into a thriving rural community as a result of Hunt's success. In the neighbourhood of the works, over a hundred terraced houses were built by the firm for a workforce that numbered 300 at the end of the century. Further sums were provided for social facilities,

Members of the smiths shop at Ransomes Orwell Works,
Ipswich, in 1889.

including two village halls, and a building programme for the local
grammar school, to mark the Queen's diamond jubilee in 1897, that
ultimately swallowed up £10,000 of Hunt's own money.

Reuben Hunt was 91 at his death in 1927 and had become the grand
old man of the agricultural engineering industry. His working association with the family business had begun in 1851 and took in a visit
to the Great Exhibition of that year. Chelmsford in 1856 saw his first
appearance at a Royal Agricultural Show, while the Smithfield
connection was even longer, for in 1913 he was presented with a
special award for attending sixty consecutive shows. There is no
doubt that the ability of the firm to prosper and develop, in spite of
the ups and downs of trade both at home and overseas, was due in
large part to the drive and acumen of Hunt himself. Following the
greater emphasis on colonial trade once the raising of tariff barriers
had made business more difficult in Europe, Hunt himself made the
long journey to Australia in 1887 for the purpose of gathering

knowledge at first hand about how best to develop that market further. He was away for ten months in all, travelling 35,000 miles in the process, and sending back to the Atlas Works a steady stream of new orders. On his return to Earls Colne, the church bells rang, the town turned out to cheer him and he was met by a delegation of grateful workers who presented him with a welcoming address in recognition of his efforts to prolong the security of their employment.[4] Reuben Hunt was a survivor and so too was the family firm. Three sons followed him into the business to provide a sense of continuity at the top that was a key to survival during the depression of the interwar years. The name remains in being, as Christy Hunt Engineering, still operating out of the Atlas Works and still with a product line partly composed of small feed-processing equipment for which there has been a steady market in the Third World.

Hunt was in the middle ranking of a league of firms based in the eastern counties that came to dominate the agricultural engineering industry during the nineteenth century. The importance here of arable farming, with its greater requirements for implements and machines, accounted for the rapid growth of local firms and gave them the capacity to seek wider markets. Ransomes, of course, was never far from the centre of these developments.[5] In the second half of the century, the firm concentrated once more upon farm machinery after being occupied with more general engineering work in the depression years after 1815. By a combination of astute management and flair for technical innovation, it consolidated an already strong position to become renowned internationally for steam engines and threshing machines while the reputation of its ploughs remained unsurpassed.

RANSOMES OF IPSWICH

At the Ransomes' Orwell Works, amongst the largest and best equipped in the country, the plough shop was said in 1886[6] to be turning out 10,000 ploughs annually, ranging from the refined Newcastle Series, used in high-quality English work, down to the much simpler implements designed for India and light enough to be carried on a man's shoulders. The export trade was vitally important in the last quarter of the century for there was no other way a firm of this

Portable steam engine specially adapted to burn straw and
other similar material in countries where coal was not readily
available. Ransomes began building these engines in the
early 1870s.

size, and with stiff competition from others, could hope to maintain
prosperity on the stagnating and relatively confined home market
alone. So it was that wood- or straw-burning steam engines were
devised for countries where coal supply was difficult, that threshing
machines were built big enough for the great Russian plains and small
enough for Mediterranean holdings, and that the product line reflected the differing climates and agricultures of the world. The
complex marketing operation embraced a global network of agents,
the printing of catalogues in many foreign languages, and repre-
sentation at scores of overseas exhibitions and trade fairs. Bearing in
mind the slow and precarious lines of communication, to receive an
order from perhaps one of the more remote areas of South America
or India, arrange for its successful dispatch and, above all, ensure that
correct payment was made must have been a considerable logistical
triumph.

RICHARD GARRETT OF LEISTON

Elsewhere in Suffolk, other names strove with some success to shine beneath the Ransomes' shadow. Leading them was the family firm established by Richard Garrett, himself the son of an implement maker, in Leiston in 1778. Initially, small edge tools for farm use were the mainstay but stiff competition from Sheffield manufacturers and the broadening market potential of the Napoleonic War period led to diversification and a tentative entry into threshing machine production in 1806. Forty years later, patent horse-powered portable threshing machines occupied a prominent position in the Garrett catalogue, second only to seed drills with fore-carriage steerage, in the development of which the firm had played an early and important part. A more widespread application of steam to threshing in the second half of the century brought Garrett portable engines to the fore to win international acclaim. Although there was a comprehensive range of field implements and small processing machines as well, the steam threshing sets and seed drills remained the principal source of Garrett's continuing reputation. Non-agricultural business was also substantial and in the 1870s included steam engines and boilers for industrial application together with diverse items such as sugar-refining machinery for Australia.

Commonly, a key personality played a crucial role in a firm's growth to maturity. At Garretts it was Richard, grandson of the founder, who set the new course for expansion from the comparatively small business that he inherited in 1836 to the giant concern employing 500 men that he passed on to his sons in 1855. He himself was no mean engineer, with an impressive list of patents to his name, but also an astute manager and businessman. From its early stages, he was involved with the then English Agricultural Society and an exhibitor at the first show in Oxford. Over the following twenty years, Garrett was a regular prizewinner, both here and at the international exhibitions, until disillusionment with the prize system operated by the Royal caused a withdrawal in 1859 from further competition. Knowledge gained of American methods of flow-line production at the Great Exhibition led Garrett in 1852 to construct the Long Shop at Leiston, a purpose-designed structure for the assembly of portable engines. This building has more recently been

175

Portable, horse-powered threshing machine of the 1840s by
Garrett of Leiston in Suffolk. The equipment is here shown
loaded for transport with the small threshing machine at the
front and the dismantled horse gear behind.

converted into a museum associated with Garretts and the development of agricultural engineering.

The 10-acre site that constituted the Leiston Works in 1870[7] was
linked by tramway to a nearby branch line of the Great Eastern
Railway. Trucks were drawn up the incline into the yard by a winding
drum driven by a steam engine that also supplied power to the
foundry. Extensive wood- and metal-working shops included a
smithy with one hundred hearths, a foundry with three cupola
furnaces capable of producing 10 tons of cast iron each day, and a
sawmill equipped to handle massive trunks of oak, ash and beech.
Output of steam engines and threshing machines alone was reckoned
at eight per week, irrespective of other orders that were in hand. This

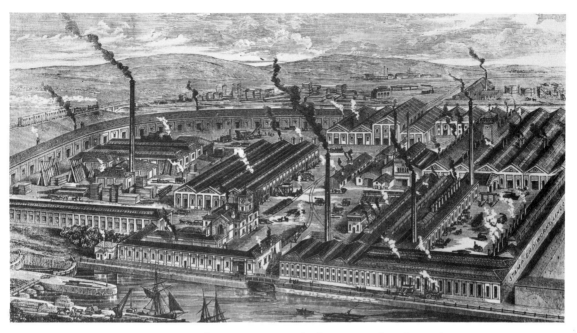

Late nineteenth-century view of Clayton & Shuttleworth's
great Stamp End Works in Lincoln.

great enterprise kept most of the able-bodied men of the village in
work and in return was able to supply some material comforts, such
as pumped water and gas lighting, into their homes.

If Eastern England dominated the Victorian agricultural engineering
industry, then Lincolnshire was its capital. The city of Lincoln itself
was the home of some world-renowned operators while a host of
smaller concerns managed to coexist with them, assisted by the
presence of a highly skilled local labour force. Clayton & Shuttleworth's Stamp End Works sprawled across 25 acres of the city and
enjoyed extensive rail and waterway communications that gave easy
access to inland markets and coastal ports. By 1897[8] total production
of 31,000 agricultural steam engines and 29,000 threshing machines
was being claimed since 1845, when the two brothers-in-law, Natha-
niel Clayton and Joseph Shuttleworth, had first experimented with
portable engine design. They had also opened factories abroad to
concentrate on the potential of central and eastern Europe; of these
the Landstrasse Works in Vienna was the most important and with
the others in Pesth, Prague and Cracow employed a total of 1,000
men to complement the 1,800 based in Lincoln.

A Clayton & Shuttleworth portable single cylinder steam
engine from the 1882 catalogue.

Smaller in size but still of international stature was the Lincoln
firm started by William Foster in 1856 which proved very successful
in the manufacture of steam engines of all kinds together with a range
of threshing and other agricultural equipment. Fire necessitated the
rebuilding of Foster's Wellington Works in 1898 and the result was a
fine illustration of late Victorian methods of organised production.
Following American practice, many of the individual machines in the
complex were driven by separate electric motors to give much greater
flexibility than was possible with conventional forms of belt drive
from a single, very large steam engine. The electricity was in turn
generated on site by two specialist high-speed steam engines. The
boilers were fired on sawdust, which was automatically collected in
the sawmill and blown by a fan along ducting to the boilerhouse.
Throughout, the physical location of departments, whether for
wood- or metal-working, was guided by the logical sequence of
production so that in effect raw materials went in at one end of the
works and made their way through to appear as finished products at
the other.[9]

178

THE HORNSBYS OF GRANTHAM

A little over twenty miles south of Lincoln is Grantham, where in 1815 Richard Hornsby, a wheelwright by training, went into partnership with a Mr Seaman to make seed drills, horse-powered threshing machines and other agricultural equipment. Hornsby subsequently became sole proprietor and on his death in 1864 the business passed to his sons Richard, James and William. Of the three, James was an accomplished engineer and had helped his father earn fame from the late 1840s for steam engines and seed drills. In 1848, the judges at the York meeting of the Royal Agricultural Society awarded the prize to a Hornsby portable engine because 'it was stronger, steadier, better fitted, got up the steam and worked with less fuel than any other engine exhibited'.[10] It went on to win the highest honour, the Council Medal, in this class at the Great Exhibition and by 1865 further medals at international exhibitions in London, Paris, Vienna, Hamburg, Cologne and Stettin. Likewise, the seed drills enjoyed comparable success, including the Great Medal at the Crystal Palace for the best corn and seed drill. This was a steerage drill available in sizes from five to thirteen rows with the novel optional feature – which aroused much interest and some doubt at the time – of flexible rubber tubes rather than conventional interlocking tin cups for the distribution of seed.

While steam engines and threshers retained their importance, in other respects the Hornsbys moved into new territory in the second half of the century. For one thing, they started making ploughs in 1859 and their distinctive wrought-iron frames and convex mouldboards were soon winning significant sales both at home and abroad. Colonial and continental markets were offered simple single ploughs of light construction while for the more sophisticated domestic farmer the firm had by the 1870s mastered a speciality in two-, three- and even four-furrow horse ploughs. It started with the Great All England Ploughing Contest held in 1871 at Reepham in Norfolk, where Hornsby picked up both prizes for double-furrow ploughs in front of all the other major makers. Over the years, the range was extended as more light-land farmers took to the multi-furrow plough in an effort to overcome manpower shortages at peak times of the year. The other major departure in this period was a concentration on

Reuben Hunt (1836–1927)
of Earls Colne.

Richard Garrett III (1807–1866)
under whose leadership the
Leiston Works achieved
international recognition.

James Hornsby (1836–1910).

James Howard (1821–1889).

The Great Exhibition Prize Corn Drill by R. Hornsby &
Sons of Grantham. Two notable features were the use of
indiarubber for the seed tubes, and rack and pinion steerage,
operated by the man shown, to facilitate the task of sowing
straight rows. From the catalogue of 1852.

the new potential of harvesting machinery. The 1870s saw Hornsby-
patent mowers and reapers, of both the manual delivery and self-
raking variety, achieve an unrivalled tally of awards at trials and
exhibitions in Britain, Europe, Africa, Australia and South America.
Intensive work at the end of the decade was devoted to the intricacies
of a mechanised knotting apparatus and finally bore fruit in Hornsby's own patented version of the sheaf-binding harvester. It was
triumphant in the two subsequent major trials of binders organised
by the Highland and Agricultural Society of Scotland in 1882 and the
Royal Agricultural Society in 1893 and the Hornsby catalogue soon
contained glowing testimonials from satisfied customers in almost
every county.

Success of this kind, in the most complex class of field equipment,
necessarily implied the fullest use of advanced manufacturing techniques. The Spittlegate Ironworks, which was visited by delegates
from the Indian and Colonial Exhibition in 1886, had grown into a
huge industrial showpiece covering 17 acres and employing 1,500

A Hornsby binder photographed at the works in 1892. Once
cut, the crop was taken by the revolving canvas table up and
into the sheaf binding mechanism to the left of where the
man is seated.

men. Throughout their tour, the visitors were able to observe highly
mechanised labour saving devices close at hand:

'The woodworking department was first entered, and here amongst a
multiplicity of operations we saw the canvas rollers for their binders
rendered circular and in three minutes turned out completely finished
by the machine. Near at hand, at 3 strokes, a man was enabled to take
from the tool under his direction large slotted threshing machine
boards, which to have completed otherwise would have taken fully an
hour. Planing machines and band saws here and there were running
right merrily, and a multiple drilling machine was shown producing 6
perforations simultaneously in a number of caving riddles.'[11]

In the foundry and metalworking departments, early forms of mass
production were also in evidence, allowing precision to go hand in

hand with economy. Quality engineering at an affordable price played a large part in Hornsby's successful entry before the end of the century into the new market created by the internal combustion engine. The firm's Agricultural Oil Engine was available in sizes from 2 horsepower upwards and could be put to any number of uses on the farm from pumping water to grinding meal to cooling milk.

For the Hornsbys themselves, commercial wealth brought social prestige. James Hornsby, son of Richard, the founder, managed to combine his own detailed work on development of the sheaf binder with other roles as a JP and, from 1889, Deputy-Lieutenant for Lincolnshire. His son, James William, was educated at Repton and Cambridge and gained considerable experience of trade overseas before joining the Hornsby board in 1886. He subsequently married into a prominent Staffordshire family, acquired Barrowby Grange near Grantham, and settled down to the life of a country gentleman. In two generations the wheelwrighting origins had been left far behind. It was as good an example as any of the new industrial aristocracy created during the Victorian period.

THE HOWARD BROTHERS OF BEDFORD

The Howard brothers of Bedford, James and Frederick, started out from a rather higher point in the social hierarchy but rose further as they applied a combination of engineering genius and commercial skill to their father's promising implement business and turned it into one of the world's giants. James, the principal partner, was a prodigious inventor who first came to national notice when as a 20-year-old he took to the 1841 Royal Show in Liverpool an all-iron plough of his own design, demonstrated it himself in trials, and came away with the top award. The Champion Plough came to form the cornerstone of an immense reputation for which Howard's own total of seventy patents, taken out over a thirty-year period from 1851 and covering all kinds of cultivating, harvesting and steam machinery, was in no small way responsible. An active public life took in , from 1868, a spell in Parliament, where he spoke up strongly for free trade and the rights of tenant farmers, and a turn in office as High Sheriff of the county. On his Clapham Park estate, purchased from the Earl of Ashburnham in the early 1860s, he pursued his own interests in

THE

CHAMPION PLOUGH

OF ENGLAND.

HOWARD'S CHAMPION PLOUGHS

COMBINE

THE BEST FORM WITH THE LEAST WEIGHT,

THE GREATEST STRENGTH,

WITH

THE UTMOST SIMPLICITY OF PARTS.

In the general arrangement of their ploughs, J. & F. HOWARD have always aimed not only at

simplicity, but durability, and in these respects as well as in

LIGHTNESS OF DRAUGHT,

THEIR CHAMPION PLOUGHS REMAIN UNRIVALLED.

The very versatile Howard Champion plough in the 1870s. It was suitable for two horses on light land and strong enough for three or four on heavy soils. Furthermore, different plough bodies could easily be attached to enable it to perform the various processes of paring, digging, ridging, subsoiling and potato lifting.

The Howard Britannia Works, well served by rail and water
traffic and with its own network of sidings.

modern scientific farming and became a noted breeder of prize
livestock, especially pigs.[12]

The Britannia Works in Bedford, headquarters of the Howard
empire, was built in 1856 to supersede a scattering of separate
workshops that had accumulated around the town. It enjoyed excellent communications, bounded on one side by the navigable River
Ouse and on the other by the Midland Railway, and at the time was
said to be the largest factory in the world devoted to the production
of field implements. In 1860, ploughs were being made at the rate of
one every ten minutes and it was claimed that more than 50,000 had
been sent out to home and overseas buyers since the Great Exhibition of 1851.[13] Ten years later, a report spoke of thirty railway
trucks leaving the firm's sidings every day, each carrying at least a ton
of assorted parts and implements.[14] The foundry was equipped with
three cupola furnaces that were loaded mechanically with pig iron and
fuel by means of a water hoist. Molten iron was run off into large
ladles mounted on trucks and distributed to the moulders via an

Smiths shop of the Britannia Works in the 1870s. An internal
tramway distributed material to the numerous hearths, and
machinery was driven through belts and shafting from a
steam engine just visible at the far right.

internal tramway network. Much use was made of moulding machinery, another one of Howard's own inventions, through which even
the complex and twisted contour of a reaping machine frame could be
formed quickly by relatively unskilled labour.

With little or no prospect for growth in domestic demand for
agricultural machinery over the last twenty years of Victoria's reign,
highly productive facilities of the Howard kind were kept going by
exploring export potential to the full. When some degree of prosperity did return to British farming during the first decade of the new
century, it in turn gave an additional fillip to the agricultural
engineers but the outlook over the longer term was grim. The First

186

World War not only totally disrupted those lucrative export markets but also gave foreign manufacturers, notably in America, the opportunity to move ahead in the development of the new tractor technology while their British counterparts were absorbed in munitions output. It was a double blow that left many firms in too crippled a condition to face the depression of the 1920s.

Those few that had already taken a bold stake in the internal combustion engine before the war stood perhaps a better chance of survival. Hornsby, for example, had entered this field in 1892, taken over a Stockport firm of gas engine builders in 1906, and carved out a useful market that was not restricted to agriculture. In 1918 its position was still very precarious but in that year a merger was agreed with Ruston & Proctor of Lincoln and slowly the business was rebuilt. Other firms that were too small to compete effectively, and were hopelessly wedded to the dying technology of steam, simply disappeared from the scene or now concentrated more on selling and servicing rather than making. A group of big family companies floundered together in 1919 into an ill-fated consortium, Agricultural and General Engineers Ltd, with the intention of dividing up a declining market between them and achieving efficiencies in production and marketing. A mere thirteen years later it collapsed and had succeeded only in eradicating altogether some illustrious names, among them Howard of Bedford. It was a sorry end to a great Victorian achievement.

8
Unlocking the Secrets of Scientific Agriculture

In the opening pages of the Royal Agricultural Society's first journal,[1] Philip Pusey put his finger on the mystery that was agriculture. True, the mechanics of cultivation had made considerable advances and many more mouths were being fed from the same area of land, but real understanding of the processes involved lagged far behind. Crop rotation had long demonstrated its effectiveness in turning lighter soils, hitherto of little account, into highly productive areas yet the secrets of this success were still securely locked away. When problems arose, such as deterioration of the turnip crop, answers were hard to find and further development of the system, so necessary to realise its full potential, could only be a hit-or-miss affair. For even the most basic questions, such as when and how thickly to sow wheat and with what variety of seed, an enormous array of quite contradictory and unproven advice was ready at hand. With heavy investment in manures other than the ordinary farmyard variety now becoming commonplace, the economic argument for greater exactitude was clear. The large quantities of powdered animal bone that were being applied to turnip land helped to push up the value of bone imports from £78,000 in 1832 to £254,000 only five years later. For a commodity that was by no means cheap, the farmer still faced many unknowns, including the optimum rate of application and, above all, the reason why it should apparently work well on some soils but hardly at all on others. The fact was that fundamental gaps in the knowledge of soil composition, the nature of plant growth and the link between them presented obstacles to the prospects of continued agricultural progress.

Like any good Victorian, Pusey's own faith in the ability of human inquiry to meet the challenge he had outlined was secure. What was needed, however, was stimulus, organisation and direction. As chairman of the Journal Committee of the Royal Agricultural Society he was responsible for editorial content and laid great stress upon contributions that promoted and publicised the scientific investigation of agriculture. This after all was what the Society's motto of 'Practice with Science' was all about. Hence early papers presented and subsequently published in the journal from 1840 covered a wide range of investigations, in the best amateur tradition, into the efficacy of manures, the feeding of livestock and diseases affecting crops. Interest in soil analysis produced in the first volume two long discourses based on experiment, the first from the Reverend W. L. Rham of Winkfield in Berkshire and the second, and more important one, from Professor Schubler of Tübingen University. In their discussion of specific gravities, weights and other properties of the constituent 'earths' these were aiming at the creation of more purely scientific data that might have a subsequent beneficial spin-off effect for agriculture.

A methodology, even a vocabulary, for agricultural science proper had yet to be framed so in this initial period many of the notices were from the upper levels of the farming community and drew upon simple observation to contribute to the accumulating evidence of experience. The purpose was not only to assist other farmers directly but to stimulate further studies. A typical short report was that from John Paynter of Cornwall[2] on the use of gas-water as a manure. With town gasworks springing up around the country, the 'ammoniacal liquor' remaining in the water used to cleanse gas before it was passed to the consumer had proved to be very pernicious when discharged into rivers but beneficial when applied to the land. Paynter had applied it at a rate of 400 gallons to the acre shortly before sowing barley, and found a marked improvement in both vigour of growth and yield. The results spoke for themselves even though the cause, namely the presence in the gas-water of ammonium sulphate as a source of nitrogen, was only imperfectly understood at this stage.

Quite apart from his key role in the Royal Agricultural Society, which included a year's term as president in 1840, Pusey developed his own keen personal interest in the new farming. He had succeeded to the Pusey estate in Berkshire in 1828 and here on the 300-acre home farm he managed by his own estimation to quadruple the stock of sheep and double the output of corn.[3] A central element in his scheme was a system of water meadows, created along the lines of some that had been observed in Devon, by means of which water from a nearby stream was made to flow along culverts and flood adjacent meadows. By alternate folding and flooding, dramatic results were claimed: one 20-acre meadow, for example, kept 400 sheep, half of the total flock, well supplied with feed for five months of the year and obviated the necessity of putting any land down to clover or seeds for summer grazing. It was a well organised, well equipped farm that played host over the years to a number of implement trials arranged by the Society, including the famous trial of American reapers held in conjunction with the Great Exhibition of 1851. Though no scientist himself, Pusey was as much concerned with cultivating an atmosphere conducive to scientific enquiry as he was with cultivating the land and regularly provided hospitality at his home for small informal gatherings of some of the leading practitioners in this developing field.

TIPTREE FARM

Wealthy promoters of agricultural improvement were a common feature of Victorian England but few were so controversial or aroused such conflicting feelings of admiration and scorn as John Joseph Mechi of Tiptree in Essex. Part of his problem stemmed from being a newcomer to farming. Mechi, the son of an Italian immigrant, amassed a personal fortune in London from the 1830s initially through the development and marketing of a patent razor strop. In 1841, he bought the 130-acre farm of poor quality at Tiptree in order to pursue a recently acquired enthusiasm for agriculture and immediately embarked upon a comprehensive programme of investment and modernisation to turn it into a more productive and efficient unit. A natural self-publicist, Mechi wrote extensively on the system of farming practised at Tiptree and the success with which it had been rewarded. His best known work, *How to Farm Profitably*, ran to several editions and was said to have achieved a total of 10,000 sales. It was a characteristically provocative piece of writing that was received with some scepticism within certain quarters of the agricultural community – partly because of Mechi's status as an outsider but mostly because the cost of improvements, over £6,000 in all, did not appear to make economic sense for such a small farm. This opinion was reinforced by the serious financial difficulties Mechi found himself in from 1866, leading ultimately to bankruptcy shortly

Early photograph of the 1860s with Mechi on the left proudly
showing off his fertile and productive fields. In the background is the farmstead with its steam engine chimney and
to the right of it the stackyard.

before his death in 1880, even though the root cause was the failure of
his commercial ventures in the City rather than the farm.

Nevertheless, for thirty years, from the mid-1840s to the mid-
1870s, Tiptree Farm became a Mecca for visitors from near and far,
farmers and townsmen alike, who came to see the miracle that had
been worked upon the unpromising heath. The visitors' book, now
preserved in the British Museum, records the comments of high-level
delegations of noblemen, politicians and farmers from around the
world. Mechi obviously enjoyed his self-appointed role as precursor
of a futuristic agriculture and gave his disciples detailed guided tours
of the farm. In answer to the critics, full financial breakdowns were

given of the improvements carried out and the returns they brought. Of the £6,200 spent, for example, £2,200 had been absorbed by the laying of over 80 miles of drains, new fencing, roads and landscaping. A further £2,000 was spent on farm buildings, £1,000 on a new house and £500 each on equipment and manure. The gain from this outlay could then be measured in terms of the reduced horse labour required on the farm, the increased yield of crops, the increased value of the manure, and the increased value of the stock as a result of their being better housed. Mechi's claim was that with these improvements the overall return rose from less than £5 to £10 per acre.[4]

Whether or not the Tiptree accounts told the whole story, Mechi and others like him were important because their farms were the shop windows of innovation. Leaving aside the economic arguments, Mechi had demonstrated the capacity of advanced contemporary practices to raise both the fertility of land and its output. There was no doubting the greatly enhanced condition of his farm or perhaps its lasting quality, for the same feature is still evident to those who work that land today. When James Caird recalled a visit to Tiptree in mid-century, he clearly preferred to maintain a diplomatic silence on the full Mechi philosophy but, having walked over every field, could 'have no hesitation in saying that for clean cultivation and healthy appearance of wheat and other crops, it is equal to any and superior to most farms we have met with in this county'.[5]

Much more unqualified praise came from Elihu Burritt, a touring American farmer, who called in at Tiptree in 1863. He believed that Mechi's enthusiastic adoption from the beginning of tile drainage, deep cultivation and steam power had provided encouragement to many others who may otherwise have lacked the confidence to embrace change. Special mention, however, was reserved for Mechi's latest method of irrigation with liquid manure. All waste from the livestock buildings drained into a large underground tank, where it was liquified by the addition of water and then, with the aid of a steam pump, distributed around the farm through a combination of iron tubing and hoses. The system required three men to operate it but enabled every field to be treated at a rate of about 100 tons to the acre. Noting that as a result fields of clover and rye-grass could be mown three or four times in one season and afterwards grazed by sheep, Burritt agreed with the proposition that town sewage might be used in the same way 'for saturating millions of acres in Great Britain with the millions of tons of manurial matter that have hitherto blackened and poisoned the rivers of the country on their wasteful way to the sea'.[6] The mechanics of some later nineteenth-century sewage farms did indeed bear some similarity to what had been instituted at Tiptree.

In that first journal article of his, Philip Pusey had argued the case for a series of experimental farms dotted around the countryside deliberately operating at the frontiers of agricultural practice and properly equipped to both extend the scope of current scientific knowledge and provide guidance to the ordinary working farmer. It was an idea that had already surfaced elsewhere – notably in a book, *On the Nature and Property of Soils*, by John Morton, which first appeared in 1838. With an extensive background in farming and land management both in his native Scotland and in England, Morton's credentials as an agriculturist of repute were far more acceptable than those of J. J. Mechi, the City of London alderman. His work on soils, high in analysis and embodying a novel system of classification, led him to the advocacy of a network of example farms, up to two or three on each of the main geological formations, to explore the mode of cultivation best suited to the different districts. In every case a full assessment would be made of the return made on capital invested, detailed daily records of work would be kept and monthly open days organised to bring in the farmers of the area, for 'the only way in which an improvement is to be effected in their mode of cultivation is by keeping a practical specimen of the best farming constantly under their view'.[7] Methods that had been successfully tried and tested on the example farm would be awarded an official seal of approval to give landlords the moral courage to galvanise their tenants into action and follow suit.

THE WHITFIELD EXAMPLE FARM

This, then, was the theory behind the Whitfield Example Farm project that Morton initiated in 1838. As agent for the Earl of Ducie's Tortworth estate in Gloucestershire, he took over personal control in that year of the 232-acre Whitfield Farm, Cromhall, from the previous tenant, George Thomas, and organised a complete restruc-

Morton's Whitfield Example Farm near Cromhall in Avon.
This was the processing part of the site with a steam engine
and threshing machine at the end, beyond the horse trailer,
and storage and preparation areas for straw, chaff and roots
in the rooms adjacent. On the other side of this building
was a large open cattle yard with shelter sheds and a
smaller area for sheep.

turing programme. It proved to be a considerable undertaking for the
holding was in a thoroughly unimproved state, having inadequate
buildings, appalling roads, no underground drainage, only three of its
forty-six fields over 8 acres in size and a haphazard system of
cropping. In the course of the next four years a transformation was
made, with a new farmstead incorporating the latest in processing
and manure treatment facilities, a logical arrangement of well drained
and fenced fields of 10 acres apiece, and a six-year cycle of rotation
that operated through three versions around the farm according to
whether the underlying soil was sandy loam, clay or limestone.
Successive editions of Morton's book on soils included in the appen-
dices first a full outline of the proposals for Whitfield, with estimates
of cost, and subsequently a progress report down to the early summer
of 1842.[8]

194

As the work progressed, Whitfield certainly emerged as a show-piece farm, to which scores of curious farmers from the surrounding district paid their respects by tramping its fields and inspecting its buildings. The cost, however, was very great. Morton's original estimate of £3,500 for the capital improvements spiralled upwards to reach a figure only just short of £8,000, although some of the overshoot was offset by £3,000 worth of timber that was realised through the clearance of hundreds of hedgerow trees when the fields were enlarged. This left the thorny question of profitability, and here Morton, for all his meticulous attention to the accounts, had in reality come no nearer to solving the fundamental problem of how the rental of an improved farm could give the landowner an adequate return on his substantial outlay without crippling the tenant with an excessive rent and undermining the whole purpose of the exercise. It would not be fair to put down Whitfield, Tiptree or the other farms in this category as failures, because they clearly did make their mark upon the farming public of the day. Yet the drawback they shared was that they fell between two stools. They were neither example farms in the true sense with an affordable model of improvement and cultivation that could be adopted lock, stock and barrel on the ordinary tenanted farm, nor were they fully fledged experimental stations conducting investigations organised along strictly scientific lines to extend the boundaries of practical agricultural knowledge. Consequently, they were prone to criticism for non-achievement on both counts.

While these limitations were working themselves to the surface, there were other voices to be heard arguing for a more outright scientific approach. Amongst them was that of Charles Daubeny, Professor of Rural Economy at Oxford, who believed that the only real way to adjudicate between the confusing variety of practices in different areas and under different conditions was to promote a more thorough understanding of the nature of the soil and the means by which its condition could be ameliorated. His own control experiments, conducted from the early 1830s, investigated plant nutrition and suggested that the mere presence of an essential nutrient in the soil was not enough to ensure growth: what mattered was how much of it was in a form suitable for the plant to accept. In an article of 1842,[9] he ventured into a deeper appreciation of the way manures operate by approaching a definition of what much later became known as the law of the minimum. Repeated dressings of nitrogen-rich manure to turnips, for example, had a diminishing effect because the soil was deficient in something else, such as phosphoric acid, not because it had become 'tired' of the nitrogen, as hitherto assumed. Healthy and productive plant growth, therefore, required that the main fertilising ingredients be in balance; animal manure was so successful not only because it contained all these vital substances but did so in a mode that could be readily assimilated by the soil.

In this way Daubeny was piecing together an eminently workable theory but at the same time, and by his own admission, he was raising more questions than answers. As the persistence of large areas of ignorance was in part due to the lack of sufficient available data, it was his view that the Royal Agricultural Society should establish an experimental farm to fill this need and so find out more about how manures work and in what precise quantities they should be used. The experiments into all manner of crop-growing and livestock-rearing matters that were being conducted around the country by eager farmers and landowners lacked too deeply the rigour of scientific discipline, and were flawed by too many variables, for any significant conclusions to be safely drawn from the results.

ROTHAMSTED MANOR

In the event, it was not the Royal Agricultural Society but a private individual who established an experimental farm run firmly along scientific lines that proved of incalculable benefit to agricultural development over the rest of the century and beyond. John Bennet Lawes was 20 when he returned in 1834 to take up residence on the family estate at Rothamsted Manor in Hertfordshire and assume control of its 250-acre home farm. The two previous years he had spent uneventfully at Oxford, without a degree, except that he had attended some of Daubeny's lectures and been fired with an interest in chemistry. Accordingly, a rudimentary laboratory was set up in the manor house for the purpose of conducting experiments into the medicinal properties of certain plants. In the later 1830s, his attention turned to agricultural analysis, and to manures in particular, following his own disappointing experience of applying bone dust to turnip land compared with its efficacy as a fertiliser on other soils

Unloading barges of imported mineral phosphate at the Lawes
Chemical Works by the Thames at Deptford in the late
nineteenth century.

elsewhere. The problem was a common one on clayland farms and
was a matter of some comment, for it restricted the value of rotation
and impaired the balance of the mixed farming system.

By 1839, Lawes was making progress. He knew that the calcium
phosphate contained in bones existed in an insoluble and inaccessible
form which only naturally acidic soils were able to break down into
the mono-calcic variety that plants could assimilate. If, however, a
conversion into what was known as superphosphate was performed
beforehand, by mechanically treating the bones with sulphuric acid,
then the manure could now expect to be beneficial on any soil.
Further trials on experimental turnip plots at Rothamsted over the
next three years confirmed these conclusions and revealed details of
the quantities of acid required; they also showed that superphosphate could be readily obtained from naturally occurring rock

197

phosphate by the same process. This was crucial, for the supply of bones was inadequate to meet any significant increase in agricultural demand and large deposits of mineral phosphates were beginning to be exploited on the continent, particularly in France and Spain. Lawes was granted a patent in 1842 for the manufacture of super-phosphate and almost immediately went into production from a factory by the Thames at Deptford. Not only was the business in itself profitable, but successful litigation brought by Lawes against infringement of his patent left him in receipt of regular royalty payments from other manufacturers. He sold his stake in 1872 for £300,000 but the firm continued to operate under the title Lawes Manure Company until 1969.

From its early days, the superphosphate works furnished Lawes with a level of financial security that enabled him to indulge further his interests in agricultural science and to turn his farm into an experimental station dedicated purely to the advancement of know-ledge. The object in his view was to put scientific investigation to work for the benefit of practical agriculture:

'Ask the most experienced farmer to explain the principles which govern the routine he is daily in the habit of practising. Ask him to determine the value of any rotation of crops or their comparative exhausting powers. Ask him what ingredients must be restored to the soil to keep its fertility unimpaired. Or the exact manner in which climate influences his produce. His answers will be vague and unsatis-factory. But these and a thousand other questions of a similar nature, are capable of solution by science and they must be answered before agriculture can be said to rest upon a satisfactory foundation.'[10]

In 1843, Lawes took as his assistant Joseph Henry Gilbert, a 26-year-old chemist whose training had included spells with the celebrated Justus Von Leibig, Professor of Chemistry at Giessen University, and Professor A. T. Thomas of London's University College and an early mentor of Lawes himself. It was the beginning of a brilliant partnership lasting for over half a century. On the one hand there was Lawes, the country squire, practical agriculturist and scientist in the amateur tradition eager to demolish prejudice or ignorance wherever it lay. On the other was Gilbert, the totally professional, totally singleminded and obsessive experimental analyst relentless in his

Philip Pusey (1799–1855).

John Joseph Mechi (1801–1880).

Sir John Bennet Lawes Bt.
(1814–1900).

Sir Henry Gilbert (1817–1901).

pursuit of accuracy. The accumulated fruits of their work, published in 174 voluminous and sometimes exhaustive reports and articles, gave a solid foundation of science to the common practice of farming. They also brought world-wide recognition and a baronetcy and knighthood respectively.

Field trials and laboratory investigations, carried out initially in an old barn converted for the purpose, were the basis of the Rothamsted experiments. Once procedures had been established, the field plots were given the same treatments in the same precisely measured quantities year after year so that, from the build-up of data, inaccuracies due to human error or variations due to climatic factors could be ironed out and firm, unequivocal conclusions confidently drawn. Gilbert's passion for meticulous detail, recording everything that could be recorded, was responsible for the consistency that became the Rothamsted hallmark and for the continuation of the experiments in later years when the interest of others, including Lawes, at times showed signs of lagging. The effect of manure on plant growth was the primary purpose of the earliest experiments, beginning in a small way with farmyard manure on wheat and turnips but thereafter taking in additional crops and mineral fertilisers as well. By dividing the land into a sequence of control plots, comparisons could be made between the different inputs used on their own, in varying quantities, and in combination, to allow a realistic assessment of nutritional requirements.

The most famous of the Rothamsted fields, Broadbalk, extends to 11 acres and in 1843 was put down to wheat in a series of narrow half-acre strips separated by access paths. With some alterations, it has remained as a continuous wheat experiment ever since, making it a most important site in the history of agricultural science. One of the strips was treated with no manure at all, another with farmyard manure, another with a mixture of the mineral fertilisers phosphorus, potassium, sodium and magnesium, another with sodium nitrate, another with superphosphate and ammonium sulphate, and so on. In the same year, the 8-acre Barnfield was put down to turnips and, apart from a short break in the 1850s, stayed that way until 1876, when it was switched to mangolds. Here two lines of plots ran down and across the field at right angles to each other to allow more scope for carrying the permutations of mineral and nitrogenous dressings. This criss-cross, or factorial, system was likewise employed on Hoosfield,

5 acres next to Broadbalk, which was under continuous barley from 1852, while from 1848 to 1951 two four-course rotations, one with clover or beans and the other with a bare fallow, were run concurrently on the 3-acre Agdell field using nitrogen and mineral manures. Experiments on hay began in 1856, using 7 acres of the old estate parkland which were separated off into plots to observe effects on both bulk and competition between the natural grasses. Maintenance of order and precision amongst this complex patchwork was the responsibility of a team of young local workers hand-picked by Gilbert and trained to operate not as farm labourers but as technicians in an open-air laboratory.

The early results on turnips and wheat provided Lawes and Gilbert with the necessary ammunition to puncture the more provocative of the theories published by Liebig in 1840, which had immediately become the subject of controversy. Working chiefly from laboratory rather than field evidence, he had stated that plants derive their supplies of nitrogen from the air, not the soil, and that all they really required by way of fertiliser were substances containing the mineral constituents, such as sodium, calcium and phosphate, found to varying degrees in the plant structure. This was perplexing to anyone using nitrogenous manures, like the ammonia-rich Peruvian guano or the Chilean nitrate now being imported in huge tonnages, and some attempts were made to accommodate their beneficial qualities within the Liebig hypothesis. At Rothamsted, however, the Broadbalk experiments clearly demonstrated the value of supplying nitrogen to the soil in order to increase wheat yields and Lawes lost no time in forthright publication of the findings:

'The theory advanced by Liebig, that crops on a field diminish or increase in exact proportion to the diminution or increase of the mineral substances conveyed to it in manure is calculated so seriously to mislead the agriculturist that it is highly important its fallacies should be generally known. The contempt which the practical farmer feels for the science of agricultural chemistry arises from the errors which have been committed by its professors. They have endeavoured to account for, and sometimes to pronounce as erroneous, the knowledge which ages of experience have established; and they have attempted to generalise without the practical data necessary to accomplish their ends with success. Agriculture will eventually derive the most important assistance from chemistry, but before it can propose any changes in the established routine of the farmer, it must, by a series of laborious and costly experiments, explain this routine in a satisfactory manner.'[11]

At this stage, the behaviour of the Leguminosae family of plants, including clover, lucerne and peas, presented an anomaly that could not be explained. The means by which they were apparently able to fix nitrogen from the air was more fully understood following the disclosure by the German chemists Hellriegel and Wilfarth in 1886 of their studies on micro-organisms in the root nodules. Bacterial activity in the soil, and its role in chemically converting substances into a suitable form for plant absorption, had emerged as an entirely new branch of scientific inquiry and at Rothamsted a young chemist, Robert Warrington, had been working in this area since 1877.

The significance of the changes to which Lawes and Gilbert made such an enormous contribution was that the phenomenon of crop growth could now be satisfactorily described in the language of chemistry. Nor was it a hollow scientific exercise, for they had demonstrated through their field experiments the varying nutritional needs of different crops and how deficiencies in the soil could be made up by precise applications of specific fertilisers rather than the hit-or-miss approach of old. In short, they made a fuller understanding of soil management a necessity for any forward-looking farmer. Even so, this was only one aspect of their work, for experiments on farm animals, starting in 1847, furthered the same kind of systematic balance-sheet approach to such matters as the relative value of different stock feeds in terms of live-weight gain, manure production and milk yield. The output had been prodigious and even though the pace slackened considerably during the 1890s, with both Lawes and Gilbert now over 70, nevertheless the celebrations in 1893 marking half a century of continuous investigation saw Rothamsted honoured as a national institution. In fact, all this time the research station had been personally funded by Lawes himself and in 1889 he had set up a trust with a further £100,000 of his own money to ensure its continuation beyond his death. Thereafter, in the twentieth century, governmental support was more forthcoming and a public appeal enabled the whole estate to be acquired in 1934, when financial pressures obliged the Lawes family to sell.

WOBURN EXPERIMENTAL FARM

Rothamsted was joined in 1876 by the Woburn Experimental Farm when the Duke of Bedford financed the conversion of Crawley Mill Farm on his estate into a small research station. It was a development prompted by the passing of the Agricultural Holdings Act in 1875, which had established the legal right of tenant farmers to compensation for the value of unexhausted manure left in the soil at the end of their term. As some areas already had local agreements of this sort in operation, the new law was the culmination of considerable lobbying to apply a similar but uniform standard across the country and give tenants the security necessary to farm responsibly. This was all very well provided the comparative value, in manurial terms, of the common varieties of purchased livestock feed could be accurately assessed. The provisions of the Act were based upon tables drawn up by Lawes and Gilbert using data collected at Rothamsted. Whether the same findings could cover light-land farms as well was one of the questions the duke hoped could be answered by trials at Woburn. The farm was handed over to a special committee of the Royal Agricultural Society with control of the scientific work exercised jointly by Lawes and Dr Augustus Voelcker, consultant chemist to the Society. The latter subsequently took sole charge and at his death was succeeded by his son, Dr J. A. Voelcker.

At the outset, a specially designed cattle feeding house was constructed on the farm. It contained a number of individual boxes each with a sunken floor to ensure full retention of all liquid and solid waste. Careful weighing and analysis of everything consumed brought forward comparative data on the weight-gain properties of different feeds and their conversion into manure of known quantity and chemical composition. Its beneficial action upon the soil could then be tested in the field trials. Of the farm's total of 131 acres, only three fields were involved in experiments and the 27-acre Stackyard field was by far the most important. Beginning in 1877, and in connection with the compensation question, 16 acres were given over to assessing the effect of organic manures made from different foodstuffs upon an ordinary four-course rotation. The results showed that while cotton cake, for example, had a higher manurial value than maize meal the average annual increase in yield per acre, of

Original buildings for the Woburn Pot-culture Station
established in 1898 at Crawley Mill Farm. In the brick
structure was a laboratory and office with a glass-house
to the left leading to a wire enclosure since removed.

13cwt of roots and half a bushel of barley, was insufficient to justify
the extra cost.[12] They also showed that neither manure had any
significant direct impact upon the wheat yield because the most
telling factor here was the quality of the immediately preceding crop
of clover.

Experiments on the continuous growing of wheat and barley, with
and without various organic and mineral manures, were conducted in
small plots on a further 5-acre portion of the same field. Amongst the
conclusions being drawn after twenty years of operation were that
the natural fertility of this soil, when cultivated but unmanured,
produced an annual yield of around 15 bushels of wheat per acre, that
the figure was unaffected when minerals alone, such as phosphoric
acid or soda, were added, but that it doubled when minerals were
accompanied by a supply of nitrogenous manure. Economical rates of
application were investigated, together with lasting effects, for the

The Woburn Pot-culture Station in 1900 showing the pots
arranged on trucks for ease of transfer from the wire
enclosure into the glass-house. From the *JRASE* of 1900.

soluble nitrogenous salts could be washed out of the soil within a
season whereas organic manures remained to give a reduced benefit
over a longer period of time. It was much the same work as had been
carried out at Rothamsted but the differences in location and soil
gave important comparative data. Since 1926, the two institutions
have been directly aligned and Stackyard field has continued its trials
to the present day.

A distinctive feature of Woburn was its inauguration in 1898 of the
first regular pot-culture station in this country following examples
set by German chemists. It was sited close to the farm buildings and
consisted of a brick-built laboratory and a lean-to conservatory with
an adjoining, and entirely wired-in, enclosure. The floors of these last
two were laid with parallel sets of tramways to allow the rows of pots
arranged on flat trucks to be moved easily from under glass into the
open air and back. Experiments using plants grown in pots had a
number of advantages over the standard field trials. For one thing,
extremes of climate, attack by insects or birds and fluctuations in

water supply could be eliminated. Secondly, whereas the soil in a field might vary from one part to another, each pot could either contain exactly similar or completely different soil types according to the dictates of the experiment. For scientific purposes, it was altogether a much more flexible medium, albeit an artificial one that could never supplant the need for continued trials in the natural field environment. The earliest work of the station sprang from the researches of E. H. Wills, by whose bequest the station itself was built, into the significance of the less known ash constituents of plants. There were other investigations in the early years of more practical relevance, including, for wheat and barley, the relative merits of thick or thin sowing, of large or small or hard or soft seed, and of pre-sowing treatments for smut.

AGRICULTURAL COLLEGES

The more light the work of the experimental stations threw onto the complexities of agricultural science, the more pressing was the need for an educational structure to introduce a rising generation of farmers to the new knowledge. Compared with the continent of Europe, the concept of the agricultural college was slow to take shape in England due at least in part to the absence of financial support from the State. Since the end of the eighteenth century there had been a Professorship in Rural Economy at Oxford but its main contribution had been in research rather than the teaching field, and it was not until much later that agriculture had any formal place in university curricula. The charter of 1845 inaugurating the first agricultural college at Cirencester stated that its aim was to teach the sons of tenant farmers 'the science of Agriculture and the various sciences connected therewith, and the practical application thereof to the cultivation of the soil, and the rearing and management of stock'.[13] Three years before, the ball had been set rolling by the local farmers' club, Lord Bathurst came forward with the offer of a 400-acre farm, and subsequently £12,000 was raised through public subscription. In fact, an overambitious start meant that the early history of the college was dogged by financial problems and, to rub salt into the wound, when James Caird visited in 1850 he found that most of the sixty students were the sons of professional rather than farming

John Cristopher Augustus Voelcker (1822–1884). A
German by birth, he was appointed Professor of
Chemistry at the Royal Agricultural College in
1849 and Consulting Chemist to the RASE in 1857.

families. Nevertheless, he was favourably impressed by the operation
and believed that 'the assistance of Government in extending similar
institutions in various parts of the country, could not be given to any
other educational purpose of greater public importance'.[14]

The college was made up of a main complex housing the accommodation and lecturing facilities, a separate laboratory in a converted
barn, and the farm. It has often been a matter of debate, both then
and since, whether an educational farm should be primarily a profitable exponent of best practice or a teaching or a research establishment. Cirencester set out, not altogether satisfactorily, to combine
all three. It was equipped with an extensive range of buildings,
incorporating a steam-powered threshing and processing area, piggeries, cattle boxes, implement sheds and slaughterhouse, rather in
the manner of the more prestigious home or example farms. During
the 1850s a good deal of experimental work was carried out here by
Dr Augustus Voelcker, who had been appointed College Professor of

The College Farm at Cirencester, dating from 1845. In the
centre, the now shortened chimney marks the original site
of the steam engine and boiler house with threshing and
processing area attached. A weighbridge was positioned at
the farm entrance to record for analysis weight gains in
stock from specific quantities of feed.

Chemistry in 1849. His investigations into the composition of
farmyard manure, the absorptive power of soils and the comparative
value of different forms of livestock fodder used data collected from
field and feeding trials at the farm supplemented by laboratory
studies. Actual instruction of students in the practical aspects of
agriculture was also given on the farm in the mornings, beginning at
6.30 a.m., while the afternoons were given over to formal lectures in
the college on such subjects as chemistry, botany, veterinary science
and surveying.

Efforts to extend a more uniform arrangement for agricultural
education around the country began to come together towards the
end of the Victorian period. The Technical Instruction Act of 1888
gave to local authorities the power to enter this area and it was
followed over the next few years by a limited but useful channelling of

Cheese Room in 1900 of the British Dairy Institute which
was based initially in Aylesbury but transferred to Reading
in the early 1890s.

government money to county councils to be spent either by the
councils themselves or in conjunction with other institutions. As a
direct result, the 1890s saw a flowering of new establishments
devoted to the teaching of agriculture. Colleges at Leeds and Newcastle in 1891 and 1892 were followed by the agricultural departments
of Cambridge and University College Reading in 1893 and the
opening of the South Eastern Agricultural College at Wye in 1894.
Gradually, a regional network of colleges emerged, providing not
only a high-grade, full-time training in agricultural management but
also an advisory service to disseminate and interpret current theories
to farmers at the local level. Ultimately, and chiefly early in the
twentieth century, they were joined by a subsidiary tier made up of
farm institutes, whose job it was to offer short courses on aspects of
the daily business of farming to those already in employment. This
was the pattern of development designed to raise the general level of
instruction at all levels and allow the advances emanating from the
research stations and elsewhere to percolate down through the ranks
for maximum effect.

9
Farms for an Industrial Age

There were many faces to farming in the burgeoning industrial society that was Victorian England. Only a few glimpses across the spectrum are possible here but even they reveal something of the complex relationship between agriculture and the wider urban and industrial world as it reacted to the multitude of demands made upon it and struggled for survival amid the harsh realities of economic life. Some of the links might seem surprising to the modern eye: who would have guessed, for example, that woollen waste, or 'shoddy', from Yorkshire mills was used as a manure in districts as far south as Kent.[1] Again, proximity to heavily populated and industrial areas, where there was a ready market for produce and plenty of cheap stable manure for sale, called for a special style of farming. Normal rotations were quite likely to be replaced by a heavy-cropping, heavy-manuring policy, so that in the West Riding of Yorkshire, the population of which doubled between 1800 and 1850, instances of continuous wheat growing were not uncommon at mid-century.[2]

THE EFFECTS OF COAL

In the north, too, the operational requirements of coal mining, and their effects upon the landscape, demanded a specially adapted and subservient farming system in the immediately surrounding area. Consequently, the mining companies themselves were often active participants in agriculture. One of the major problems of farming near to a pit was the subsidence that played havoc with attempts to maintain an efficient network of land drainage. Moreover, at those pits where coke was a primary product, noxious smoke issuing from the ovens all but laid waste the land lying in its path. These and similar factors explain why Messrs Strakers & Love of Brancepeth Colliery in Durham farmed a total of 587 acres in order to avoid the compensation claims for damage that they would otherwise have encountered. There was a beneficial element as well, however, for a sizeable proportion of the separate holdings were turned over to clover, grass and other fodder crops for subsequent transportation underground in large quantities to nourish the army of pit ponies at work down below.[3]

On Lord Durham's estate, two farms were in most immediate contact with the highly developed mining venture there and were accordingly under the control of his own farm manager. Of the 759 acres involved, well over half consisted of pasture, clover and meadow, but even so each year a great deal of hay, together with other feed, was bought in from outside to provide for the thousand or so ponies and horses engaged at any one time. The buildings at Bowes House Farm contained as a result much larger than average facilities for the storage and machine-processing of all this material, while both it and the other holding, Over the Hill, boasted fine quarters for the housing and fattening of stock. Perhaps not surprisingly in view of the cheap coal at hand, steam tackle formed part of the cultivating equipment and ensured the timely completion of ploughing operations in spite of the occasional dispatch of horses to lend urgent assistance at the pit-head during critical periods of the farming year.

While in one region the extraction of coal might damage farmland, in another the same coal might lead to the creation of a new and more potent agricultural landscape. Wind-driven scoop wheels had been at work in the fenland districts of eastern England since the seventeenth century, discharging water from subsidiary drains up and into the main river outfalls. However, their total dependence upon suitable wind conditions and their difficulty in lifting water to the greater heights made necessary by the steady contraction of the peat levels made them a source of growing dissatisfaction. In particularly wet seasons, and just when they were most needed, the wind might fail and carefully cultivated acres revert to swamp and be ruined in a matter of days. The task of replacing windmills with the enhanced capacity and reliability of steam began in 1820 and soon gathered momentum. One report of 1851 estimated that there were at least thirty-five steam engines operating in the Lincolnshire fens alone and that between them, raising water an average of 7ft, they were responsible for the drainage of about 80,000 acres of land.[4] As the changes spread through the fenlands, hundreds of windmills were left redundant while many of those that continued in work only did so for

Dogdyke steam drainage mill, Lincolnshire, built in 1855 to raise water by scoop wheel from the low-lying land at the right into the higher level of the River Witham on the left.

as long as no major repairs were required.

The first generation of steam drainage mills employed the standard kind of scoop wheel, often over 30ft in diameter and fitted with long wooden float-boards, which dragged water up from the lower level and pushed it through one-way mitred gates into the outfall. Centrifugal pumps appeared at mid-century and before very long, with their greater efficiency and little need for attention, were the usual choice in new installations. The improved drainage brought by the steam engine changed the nature of agriculture over much of the district because as the peat continued to shrink so the practice grew of digging out the underlying clay and spreading it over the surface. Instead of making do with fields of marshy grazing that might be inundated at any time, the farmer now had a topsoil of rich mould that would prosper under conventional rotations to give high yields of corn. The economic landscape of fenland, therefore, was also transformed. Since their later displacement, first by diesel then by

212

The beam engine at Dogdyke, now restored to working order.

electricity, most of the steam mills now exist only as evocative ruins. Dogdyke in Lincolnshire is one of a small number that have been preserved by enthusiasts and is regularly steamed on open days. Here the double-acting 16-horsepower beam-engine, in service from 1856 to 1940, turned its scoop wheel seven times each minute to raise 25 tons of water into the River Witham from the low-lying lands around Tattershall.

SEWAGE FARMING

Turning from land drainage to land irrigation or flooding, a further specialist category of Victorian agriculture emerges, namely sewage farming. The theory and practice of utilising town waste to good effect blossomed in the second half of the century only to recede shortly after as actual experience showed much of the initial optimism to have been overblown. In theory at least, sewage disposal appeared to offer real possibilities of mutual advantage to town dweller and farmer alike. Continued urban growth and the widespread adoption of the domestic water closet produced annually millions of tons of heavily diluted sewage to pollute the already filthy rivers and pose enormous risks to health. A logical alternative would be to divert the liquid onto farms, where the land itself would act as a giant purifying filter, be enriched by the organic matter it received, and more than return the costs of irrigation through the increased produce resulting. From the 1850s, J.J. Mechi was amongst the more vociferous of early converts to the cause, likening the sewage running as waste to a 'stream of liquid guano':

'When once convinced of its value, recorded registers of supply will be attached to each farm like our gasometers. Quarterly demands for its use will be cheerfully paid; our towns will be cleansed, and our country fertilised.'[5]

On the recipient farm, he envisaged a network of pipes from which the sewage would be pressure-hosed onto individual fields, in the same way as he distributed liquefied farmyard manure on his own land at Tiptree. Over the following twenty years, and consistent with other investigations of the day into aspects of agricultural science,

214

The Holme Post in Cambridgeshire. When the great Whittlesey
Mere was drained with the aid of steam power in 1852, this cast
iron column, originating from the Crystal Palace structure of 1851,
was sunk into the ground so that its top was level with the
surface. Year by year it has recorded the shrinkage of the peat soil
and today nearly thirteen feet of the column stand above
ground level.

town sewage was subject to extensive analysis as to its composition
and value as a farm manure. Most attention centred on ammonia
content, for this was the source of nitrogen, and the investigations
carried out by Lawes and Gilbert provided a more reliable level of
data than some of the other wilder estimates then in circulation. On
behalf of the Royal Commission on the Sewage of Towns, they
studied samples collected in Rugby between 1861 and 1863 and
concluded that of the 60 or so tons of dilute sewage generated per

215

The main cattle and feed house at Heathcote Farm dating from
the period when the sewage experiment was in progress.

inhabitant per year, 12½lb was in the form of ammonia. The
proportion was variable for in the wetter seasons a lot more water
would run into the sewers and weaken the solution still further.
Nevertheless, the figures appeared to suggest that the ammonia
output per inhabitant was equivalent in manurial terms to about
74lb of guano and should be priced accordingly.[6] The fallacy here
was that the nutrients were so heavily diluted that their real worth to
agriculture was reduced significantly. Many early expectations on the
economic viability of sewage farming foundered on this point.

The general conclusions arising out of the Royal Commission's
deliberations were that sewage disposal on farmland may well be a
social benefit to the towns but one that was unlikely to generate
much cash for the returns to the farmer were barely enough to
support a price of ½*d* per ton. To gain maximum effect, a distribution rate of 5,000 tons per acre per annum was recommended on
meadow or Italian rye-grass for conversion into dairy products and,
via the stock, farmyard manure which could be applied to arable land

elsewhere on the farm. The additional and considerable outlay involved in piping the sewage from town to farm made the whole system much less of a profitable enterprise in its own right which Mechi and others had anticipated, and much more of a convenient means for the community to obtain at least some contribution towards the costs of sewage disposal.

This fact was borne out by the case histories of the nine entrants in the Royal Agricultural Society's Sewage Farm Competition of 1879. The winner of Class II, for farms taking the sewage of more than 20,000 people, was at Leamington Spa in Warwickshire, where the town's reputation as a health resort had necessitated considerable expenditure on waste disposal methods.[7] After some abortive experiments with other systems, a sewage farm scheme was inaugurated in 1871, with the Earl of Warwick's Heathcote Farm, a little over two miles from the town centre, being the chief recipient. An installation housing two condensing beam-engines pumped the sewage through a rising main to a point above the farm from where it was transferred to a network of earthenware pipes and open trenches. As Mechi's method of hose distribution had by this time been abandoned, the individual fields were instead irrigated by means of overflowing parallel ditches that traversed the natural slope of the land. Four men were employed to oversee the work and a telegraph kept the farm and pumping station in direct communication with each other.

Lord Warwick paid an annual rate of £450 for the sewage in addition to meeting the not insignificant cost of maintaining all the conveyancing channels on the farm. In return, he received up to 1½ million tons of sewage per annum, representing about 1 million gallons a day, some of which was diverted to other nearby tenanted farms on the estate. For the corporation, the £450 was a useful contribution to its annual costs of over £1,000 incurred in collecting and pumping, and the clear water issuing from the sub–surface field drains showed that this method of filtration worked well. For Lord Warwick, the result was a highly productive farm of 350 acres that showed a clear profit on the revenue account but only when charges for the initial cost of conversion to the system were excluded. Most of the sewage was applied to rye-grass, at a rate in 1875 of 900,000 tons on 54 acres, and enabled up to seven crops to be gathered during the year both for sale off the farm and for stall feeding the dairy herd of 40 Shorthorns. The rest was used in periodic short bursts on

217

Blake's Lock pumping station on the River Kennet in Reading
where water turbines were employed to pipe the town's
sewage to the Corporation farms two miles away.

mangolds during their growth cycle, on land being prepared for
spring-sown corn and on small acreages of market garden crops such
as rhubarb and strawberries. All this extra care and treatment was
reflected in yields, for example the 600 gallons of milk per cow per
year, that were on the whole abundant and for which there was a
ready sale in spite of early fears of consumer resistance to produce
reared on human waste.

The last quarter of the century saw something like a hundred other
larger towns and cities launch schemes for the agricultural disposal of
their sewage. Rather than sell it to a neighbouring farmer, the more
common path followed by the big authorities was to run the whole
operation themselves from beginning to end. In the case of Reading,
the corporation had by 1875 established two farms on almost 800
acres of low-lying gravelly soil located to the south-west of the town
centre. A new pumping station, driven by three water turbines, was
built at Blake's Lock on the River Kennet to collect the sewage from

about 30,000 of the town's inhabitants and pipe it to receiving points on the farms two miles away. Here it was routed through an arterial system of underground earthenware pipes and then distributed onto the land via surface ditches. Four years after the start of the project, 76 acres were being regularly irrigated, with another 140 in preparation, at a total rate of up to 800,000 gallons per day. Again, most of the sewage was applied to rye-grass, principally for the benefit of the herd of dairy Shorthorn cows.

Substantial buildings were erected for the cattle, complete with steam-powered processing facilities and a farmstead tramway for feed distribution and removal of manure to enclosed pits for use elsewhere. Even a crude form of central heating was laid on in the piggeries by means of pipework connecting with the boilerhouse. At over £5,000 for the buildings and cottages alone, this was municipal enterprise on a grand scale but one that was still unable to operate at a profit in a bad, wet year, like 1879, even after charges for rent and sewage were excluded from the accounts. Experience showed that the economics were too shaky and the whole system too unwieldy from a managerial viewpoint to survive for very long once more efficient means of chemical and mechanical disposal had been developed. In the early decades of the twentieth century, most sewage farms, including Reading's, were replaced by treatment works established on part of the original site.

DISTRIBUTION

A more obvious and more fundamental effect of continued urban growth on the agriculture of late Victorian England was the complex and lengthening food supply chain needed to sustain the teeming multitudes. In the fruit and vegetable trade, for example, improvements in transportation drew in from overseas large quantities of everything from the common to the exotic while at the same time enabling domestic producers to streamline their operations into specialised categories to meet the demands of distant markets. Staggered ripening times brought a dovetailing of the two so that at a major centre like Manchester's Shude Hill Market, serving a population of three-quarters of a million, carrots in the 1890s were available first in April from France, then in June from Holland, followed by Bedfordshire, Lincolnshire and Huntingdonshire as the summer months passed. Similarly, new potatoes could be acquired all the year round, beginning in midwinter with consignments grown under glass in Cornwall and in the warmer air of the Canary Islands and France through to early spring, when Jersey and Guernsey filled the gap before the mainland supplies came on stream.[8] The railways were the vital arteries of this trade and there grew up around the main termini, particularly in the metropolis, extensive transit depots where produce could pass through the hands of middlemen and on to the retailers without necessarily making an appearance at the central markets.

FRUIT GROWING

The orchard coverage in England steadily increased during the last quarter of the century while the acreage under small fruit almost doubled to 63,000 in the ten years up to 1898 as many farmers deserted cereal growing in search of more profitable alternatives for which there was a growing consumer demand.[9] One was A. C. Wilkin, who occupied the 250-acre farm next to J. J. Mechi of Tiptree in Essex. In 1862 he began to turn his attention away from wheat to fruit, for the strawberry in particular thrived well on the local soil. In 1885 he entered the jam-making business, specialising in whole fruit preserves, and by the end of the century was producing about 200 tons a year using both his own and imported supplies of fruit. Another was Sir Walter Gilbey, who started experimenting with the growing of fruit on his farm at Elsenham in Essex in the 1880s. Year by year a few acres were put down to plums, pears, raspberries and strawberries and a small factory was built for the making of jam. All the produce bore the Elsenham Hall label and in 1901 was being dispatched by rail to fifty retailing outlets. The jam factory became a common feature of fruit-growing districts because it helped to overcome the problems associated with seasonal peaks when the market was overloaded with a highly perishable commodity. For this reason, in the Worcestershire town of Pershore, famous for its plums, the Earl of Coventry promoted a small jam factory next to the railway station for the benefit of his tenants on the Croome Court estate.

Small-scale buildings at Elsenham in Essex where Sir Walter
Gilbey first began making jam in the 1880s.
From *Country Life* of 1901.

Boiling room of the Elsenham jam factory in 1901.

Although in some fruit areas, notably Evesham, there were many small growers quite profitably occupying plots of less than 10 acres, the tendency nearer to London was for the trade to be in the hands of the larger operator. Before 1897, when they went their separate ways, William and Edwin Vinson controlled the biggest strawberry and raspberry enterprise in the country, occupying a total of 1,000 acres around Orpington in Kent, most of which has since been swallowed up by suburban development. A little further east, from Swanley to Sevenoaks, the Woods family partnership had 2,000 acres down to fruit, providing amongst other things 500 tons of raspberries and 150 tons of plums a year both for sale direct and for absorption, along with bought-in supplies, into their highly mechanised jam-making and bottling plant.

The most dramatic expansion in the fruit sector during the last thirty years of the century concerned the hot-house culture of varieties previously destined only for the tables of the very rich but now in great demand by the prosperous urban middle class. Precise figures are unobtainable but something like a tenfold increase in the area under glass, to 1,100 acres, was witnessed during the period, with about a quarter of this taken up by tomatoes, the commercial production of which rose from a barely recordable level to over 10,000 tons per year. The biggest growers were concentrated in a band north of London running through Middlesex, Hertfordshire and parts of Essex. The glasshouses of Peter Kay in Finchley, for example, extended over 19 acres, had cost £50,000 to erect and were heated by 27 miles of hot-water piping. From here in 1898 100 tons of tomatoes were dispatched, divided amongst several varieties so as to be available through until Christmas, together with 75 tons of grapes and 200,000 cucumbers. However, credit for the biggest glasshouse operation in the world at that time went to Joseph Rochford, whose 27 acres in Cheshunt annually yielded 400 and 140 tons of tomatoes and grapes respectively. His brother Thomas acquired a further 24 acres and in the whole district there were 125 acres of glass where in the early 1880s, when the Rochfords started out, there was just one small grower.

The distinctive shape of the milk churn answered the need for strong, hygienic and convenient containers suitable for rail transport. From a catalogue of 1900.

DAIRY FARMING

The same urban stimuli, supported by a reliable and rapid transport system, wrought great changes upon dairy farming. One of the outstanding pioneers of the railway milk trade was George Barham, who was born the son of a London dairyman and milk seller in 1836. He too became a dealer in milk on his own account and in the early 1860s began supplementing the fluctuating and sometimes filthy supplies from city herds with fresh clean milk brought in by train from outlying farms north of London. A gradual process of expansion was suddenly transformed by the 1865 cattle plague, which raced through the dairies of the capital killing many and leading to the slaughter of most of the rest in an attempt to restrict further contagion. In the event, it was an act of kindness for the lower-grade cowsheds had long surpassed in squalor even the standards then acceptable to a Victorian city and the milk that issued was often an ideal conveyor of disease. Railway activity rose to fill the gap in supply and within two years the volume of London rail-borne milk had more than doubled to an annual level of 6 million gallons. Barham expanded his capacity through agreements with Derbyshire farmers for the daily purchase of their milk, which was conveyed to King's Cross in goods vans attached to the Great Northern Railway's scheduled passenger trains.

By 1880, half a million gallons of milk a year, brought in from thirty counties, were being handled by Barham's own Express Country Milk Supply Company. Many other similar organisations grew up both in London and elsewhere to make the early morning milk train a standard feature of the urban scene. For the dairy farmer, far from a town but within reasonable proximity of a station, the prospect of a regular, secure income encouraged a more positive preference for liquid milk production over the previous dependence upon butter and cheese. The new trade required new equipment and a Barham subsidiary set up in the mid-1860s, the Dairy Supply Company, was in time able to provide all the necessary requisites from coolers and strainers on the farm to specially designed churns for railway transport and distribution cans and carts for the deliveryman in the towns.

In spite of these developments, the suburban dairy farm, retailing direct to the local inhabitants from a site close to the city centre, still held an important though now much less decisive place in the system. Furthermore, the grander examples were highly fashionable advertisements for cleanliness and purity that helped to erase from the public mind memories of disease, dirt and contamination. Perhaps the best known was Tisdall's Holland Park Farm, based on 70 acres of parkland pasture in the heart of London's Kensington. In the 1870s, new premises were constructed on the High Street, consisting of a shop for over-the-counter sales and glazed observation area where customers could observe the milking of Shorthorn cows tied up in the two rows of stalls beyond. Adjacent was a distribution depot collecting milk both from this farm and two others in Epsom for daily deliveries throughout the West End. With its decorative tiles, central fountain and marble-topped tables, the shop aimed to provide a cool, relaxing atmosphere where the genteel inhabitants of the neighbourhood could sip a glass of milk or lemonade while making their purchases. The same intention lay behind George Barham's acquisition of the 200-acre College Farm in Finchley. By the time the

Inside the Holland Park Dairy in the 1870s. On either side
are retail counters and the glazed double doors in the distance
allowed viewing of the cow stalls beyond.
From J. P. Sheldon's *Dairy Farming*, 1878.

public were admitted in 1883, a completely new set of buildings had
been constructed, including a buttermaking dairy, of the type more
usually associated with a great landed estate, and extensive accommodation areas for cattle fronted by a refreshment room equipped
with facilities for viewing the herd of assorted Guernsey, Shorthorn
and Kerry cows. Here, for the town dweller, some insight, however
idealised, could be gained into contemporary advances in farm
practice.

Of all the other developments from the period in the processing

Butter making dairy at George Barham's College Farm,
Finchley, built in the early 1880s and originally with
a thatched roof. In the 1920s it was converted to a popular
tea shop for visitors to this show-piece farm.

and marketing of milk, just one further example must suffice. The
factory process of manufacturing cheese came to England in 1870 and
the first purpose-built structure concerned, dating from the same
year, still stands complete with its inaugural bronze plaque in the
small Derbyshire village of Longford. Much comment and speculation had been aroused by the apparently successful attempts in
America to operate large-scale cheesemaking enterprises and, of the
groups most interested here, the Derbyshire Agricultural Society
took an early lead. A committee was set up late in 1869 with the task
of putting to the test the benefits claimed for the factory method.
Centralised production, it was argued, brought economies of scale,
more uniform quality and a better return to the farmer while at the
same time relieving him or his wife of the thankless task of making the
cheese in his own inferior dairy. Enough money was raised from well-
heeled sympathisers to enable the committee to set up a pilot scheme

226

Inside the Longford cheese factory. After most of the whey had
been removed, curd was run off from the milk vats on the left
into the dry vat in the middle. Any remaining whey was
drained and the curd then mixed with salt and put in the
presses on the right. From J. P. Sheldon's
Dairy Farming, 1878.

and guarantee the contributing farmers a fair price, 6½*d* per gallon,
for their milk whatever the outcome.

Accordingly, two cheese factories went into production the following year. The first was housed in a converted warehouse in Derby
itself while the other was a hastily erected structure in Longford,
built of wood to avoid damp problems, and financed by the local
landowner, the Hon. E.K.W. Coke. Though well situated in the
centre of the dairying district, the major drawback was that for
summer working the water in the adjacent stream was too warm and
cooler supplies had to be piped in from over a mile away. Both

factories in their early years were managed by Americans, the brothers Levi and Cornelius Schermerhorn, who were brought over to pass on the fruits of their experience.

The experiment was not without its initial difficulties – partly operational, necessitating some adjustments to the American procedure to allow for English conditions, and partly commercial, as dealers viewed with hostility this new threat to their influence over individual producers. Nevertheless, a measure of success was achieved and by the third year, 1872, the original controlling committee was able to withdraw and leave each factory to be run by its own co-operative of participating farmers. The Longford accounts for 1873 showed that the sale of over 86 tons of cheese, manufactured from the milk of 517 cows, together with proceeds from the disposal of butter and whey, left for the farmer a return of $7\frac{1}{2}d$ per gallon on his milk, or $1d$ more than under the earlier guarantor system.[10] With interest running high, thousands of visitors from the farming and general public alike were attracted to the factories and a number of similar projects were launched both elsewhere in the county and in the cheese districts of Cheshire and Somerset. In the second half of the decade, however, the position deteriorated sharply as the mounting level of foreign imports depressed the price of cheese at home and substantially reduced profit margins. To make matters worse, there was worrying evidence that the output of some factories, once the first flush of enthusiasm had waned, was commanding an even lower price because of a fall-off in quality. This appeared to be due not only to managerial deficiencies in the factory itself but also to the supply of warm, contaminated and even partially skimmed milk from inattentive or unscrupulous farmers. While the underlying rationale of factory production remained sound, English cheese would have to re-establish its market position and improve its quality control before further real progress could be made.

SILAGE

Back on the farm, too, the new conditions prevailing in the later nineteenth century induced a certain amount of flirtation with methods and practices imported from abroad. A good example was silage, the making of which enjoyed a strong but brief phase of popularity from the early 1880s. At a time when livestock and dairying offered a better prospect to some than corn, silage was seen as a practical solution to the problem of finding sufficient bulk feed in the winter months for a larger cattle population. After a run of disastrously wet summers, no one needed to be reminded of the hazards of making hay in the English climate, but here now was a means of achieving perhaps a better result, from both grass and other fodder crops, at a lower cost and without the same crippling dependence upon sunshine. It was an enticing offer and led to a wave of experiments on leading farms. The initial impulse came from Europe,[11] where in Germany the ensiling of mown grass had been tried at least as early as the 1840s and by the 1860s, largely through the work of M. Reihlen of Stuttgart, had extended to other fodder crops, including sugar beet leaves and maize. The French also were not far behind and it was the publication in 1877 of a manual by Auguste Goffart detailing the processes involved that really awakened agricultural consciousness to the subject in England.[12]

In 1884, when the Royal Agricultural Society's investigation into silage was published, there had already been much activity in England in the previous three years and a great deal of variation in practice was observed. The most obvious area of divergence was in the form of the silo itself. Some were pits dug into the ground with their sides lined with concrete, others were actual structures, while others again were a mixture of the two. It was also not uncommon for existing buildings to be converted for the purpose – particularly where, as in the case of a redundant barn, there was a large volume of internal space that could be subdivided into separate silage compartments. From the silo, the conflict of opinion moved on to the desirability or otherwise of chopping up the crop before storing it, on whether and how much salt should be added, on the degree of treading down required, on the amount of weight that should be applied to the heap and on the best way of feeding the actual silage to stock. The only clear fact about good silage – whether made from grass, clover, rye, oats, lucerne or whatever – was that cattle loved it.

A surviving example from the first generation of purpose-built silos exists on the home farm of what was then Lord Ashburton's Grange estate near Alresford in Hampshire. It was built in 1882 of concrete, in common with other parts of the home farm and at least one of the tenanted farms on the estate, and on a sloping site that

On the left are the concrete silos built in 1882 on the home
farm of Lord Ashburton's Grange estate in Hampshire. Access
at a higher level for loading was on the other side.

provided an upper charging and a lower emptying level.[13] Load by
load, the crop was tipped in, well trodden to exclude as much air as
possible, and then a cover of closely fitting boards was applied and
surmounted by weights to maintain a steady downward pressure.
Internally, the silo was divided into three compartments, each one
11ft square by 12ft deep, giving a total capacity of about 96 tons.

The infectious optimism that accompanied these early prototypes
was so rapidly transmitted that official reports of the mid-1880s were
able to identify well over 3,000 separate silage sites of one sort or
another around the country.[14] This very success, however, caused the
downfall of silage making in the short term, for technical knowledge
and experience lagged behind the eagerness to experiment. While the
analytical work of Dr Voelcker and others had begun to explore
scientifically the fermentation processes within the silo, this was still
some way short of providing the positive guidance necessary to
maintain control and ensure, for example, the formulation of lactic

acid, the preserver, rather than butyric acid, the destroyer. Furthermore, the nutritional value, digestibility and protein content of silage depended upon the growth stage at which it was cut and here reliable data were completely lacking. Consequently, much was left to chance and when silage moved away from the carefully monitored experiment into the very different environment of the ordinary working farm it did not take too many disappointing failures to dampen the enthusiasm. During the 1890s the retreat of silage was as fast as its earlier advance; the quest of farmers 'to extend summer into winter'[15] ended in disillusion. A new impetus came at the beginning of the twentieth century with the introduction to England of American stave silos, followed by a long period of experiment in the research establishments during and after the First World War to slowly reinstate the process as both an economic and a practical proposition.[16]

CORN

Finally, to return to corn growing, three Victorian farmers may be singled out as pointers for the future. The first, representing a coming breed of hard-headed commercial farmers, was Samuel Jonas of Chrishall Grange near Saffron Walden in Essex. He was a tenant farmer with a difference, for in 1864 his holding, consisting of five adjacent farms rented from four separate owners, ran to 3,000 acres and by 1870 had risen further to 4,200 acres. The whole principle of controlling such a huge enterprise was to take advantage of every conceivable economy by reducing unit costs of production in order to extend the margin of profit. At the central farmstead, for example, the most extensive steam-powered machinery could be kept fully employed in all the threshing, grinding and processing work that had to be done. On the land, likewise, the best use could be made of steam cultivation especially as the fields had been enlarged and squared so that none were less than 60 and some were as much as 400 acres in extent. The labour force of 100 men and 76 horses was large but smaller than if the holding had been divided into individual units; the bulk purchase of inputs, at an annual rate of £4,000 for corn and oil cake and £1,700 for artificial fertilisers such as guano and blood-manure, meant that preferential prices could be negotiated with suppliers.[17] Agriculturally, the farm was conventional in that a standard rotation was followed, large numbers of cattle and sheep were kept for their manure, and all the hay, straw and roots were consumed on the premises. It was chiefly the scale and its commercial implications that made Chrishall Grange stand out.

For the second of the three farmers, the system of cultivation rather than the size of holding was the dominant feature. John Prout took up residence in 1861 on Blount's Farm, a 450-acre holding of clayland soil near Sawbridgeworth in Hertfordshire. He had just returned from a period spent farming in Canada and immediately set about the upgrading of what had become a very run-down farm. In addition to the usual improvements to fences, field patterns and drainage, he also embarked upon a radically different cropping regime, taking as his inspiration the results of the Rothamsted field trials. While only a by-product of the main experiments, the work of Lawes and Gilbert had shown that it was possible to disregard all accepted wisdom on rotations and grow the same crop year after year on the same plot as long as the soil was regularly topped up with the correct combination of necessary nutrients. With proper management, these could be supplied equally well by artificial fertilisers as by farmyard manure, thereby rendering superfluous the maintenance of large numbers of stock and the cultivation of fodder crops for them to consume.

Prout obtained a detailed analysis of the Blount Farm soil from Augustus Voelcker, the Royal Agricultural Society's consultant chemist. The main finding was that the levels of phosphate and ammonia were most critically affected by a cereal crop and that their depletion could be avoided by annual dressings of superphosphate and nitrate of soda respectively. On this basis, Prout instituted a programme of tillage in which wheat and barley were commonly grown continuously on the same fields and played the leading role. There was no place for cattle or sheep for the only farmyard manure was provided by twelve working horses and this was applied to smaller acreages of beans and mangolds. All the remaining fertiliser was artificial and bought in and all the excess produced, including the straw, was annually sold off the farm. When Rider Haggard visited the farm, then run by Prout's son, in 1901 he was able to pronounce upon a system that had been in operation for over thirty-five years.[18] The taking of successive corn crops, he found, had not had an adverse

Samuel Jonas, agricultural entrepreneur, of Chrishall Grange.

George Baylis (1846–1936).

effect upon soil fertility for the average wheat yield over seventeen preceding years was 36 bushels to the acre, well above the norm. Perusal of the accounts, furthermore, showed that the farm had always operated at a profit, notwithstanding the years of severe depression for corn farmers. Summing up, Rider Haggard commented: 'I never saw a better arranged or, I may add, in its own fashion a better cultivated holding.'[19]

The last farmer in the trio was a hybrid who combined the commercial capacity of a Jonas with the free-thinking ability of a Prout to go back, in an agricultural sense, to the beginning and start again from first principles. This was George Baylis, a farmer's son from Evesham, who ended an inauspicious early career in 1875 at the age of 30 by borrowing the £1,500 necessary to purchase the 400-acre farm of Wyfield Manor, a few miles north-west of Newbury in Berkshire. Knowing from his own bitter experience how much time and money were normally absorbed in the keeping of animals chiefly for their manure, he too drew upon the lessons of Rothamsted and

233

resolved to cut out livestock altogether from the equation. Instead, he switched to a total reliance upon artifical fertilisers and introduced a cropping system that alternated corn with bare fallow, to cleanse the land, and included a course of clover one year in every six. Naturally, without the requirements of stock, much depended upon being able to sell off the farm not just the corn but also the hay crop and the large quantities of surplus straw produced every year. In that part of the country, however, where a range of commercial and urban outlets were available within a short distance by rail, no real problem was presented.

The Baylis method proved remarkably successful because its specialist type of corn farming, with production costs pared to the minimum, was able to make progress even during the depressed years of the century's last two decades. Working on the principle that the bigger the holding the more thinly could the overheads be spread, from the mid-1880s Baylis embarked upon a cycle of expansion as he absorbed nearby farms whose previous occupants, unwilling or unable to adapt in the face of the economic storm, had defaulted on payments, given up and gone. The land had often deteriorated to the point of being both unsaleable and unlettable so the owners were glad to offer it to Baylis on extremely favourable tenancy terms in the hope that he could do something with it. Beginning in 1885 with the 500-acre Northheath Farm in neighbouring Winterbourne, the accretions followed at frequent intervals until by the end of the century the total area farmed by Baylis had passed the 4,000 acre mark.[20] By 1917, he was firmly established as the largest arable farmer in England, with over 12,000 acres under his control scattered through Berkshire and parts of Hampshire. Moreover, a number of the farms initially occupied under tenancy agreements were subsequently purchased out of accumulating profits to the point where a little over half of the total extent was in outright ownership.

Everything about the operation was large – from the size of the ploughed fields worked by steam power to the army of 200 men and horses employed and the hundreds of tons of artificial inputs that were bought and applied each year. All were tightly controlled by a management structure that was headed by Baylis himself, at a great old age, well into the 1930s. It was not all plain sailing, for the process of running farms together, however successful agriculturally, was not without its social consequences in the areas concerned and the same

A late nineteenth-century wagon from the Baylis farms, now
at the Museum of English Rural Life.

system that worked well in the slump of the late nineteeenth century
could not escape the depths of depression that returned after the
First World War. Even so, George Baylis is a key figure in the
transition to modern concepts of agriculture. Although he himself
lived through more than fifty years of Victoria's reign, in his
approach to the commercial exploitation of the land, in farming for
profit utilising whatever benefits current scientific knowledge or
market conditions could provide, he came very close to the
contemporary image of the twentieth-century businessman-farmer.

Conversion Tables

Weights, measures and, where appropriate, sums of money have been expressed in the contemporary units.

Weights and Measures

1 ounce (oz) = 28·4 g

1 pound (lb) = 0·454 kg

1 hundredweight (cwt) = 50·8 kg

1 ton = 1·016 tonne

1 inch = 25.4mm

1 foot = 0·305 m

1 yard = 0·914 m

1 mile = 1·609 km

1 acre = 0·405 hectare

1 gallon = 4·55 litres

1 bushel = 8 gallons

1 quarter = 8 bushels

Currency

1 old penny (*d*) = 0·417 p

1 shilling (*s*) = 5 p

1 guinea = £1.05

Notes

CHAPTER 1 : FARM BUILDINGS

1   Loudon, J.C., *Encyclopaedia of Agriculture*, 1831, p. 442.
2   Caird, James, *English Agriculture 1850-1*, 1852, p. 490.
3   Morton, J.C., *Cyclopaedia of Agriculture*, 1855, p. 790.
4   Viscount Torrington, *On Farm Buildings, with a Few Observations on the State of Agriculture in the County of Kent*, 1845.
5   Thompson, H.S., 'Farm buildings', *Journal of the Royal Agricultural Society of England (JRASE)*, 1850, p. 186.
6   Andrews, G.H., *Agricultural Engineering*, 1852, Vol. 1, *Buildings*, p. 32.
7   Architects in Architecture, *Coleshill Model Farm – Past, Present, Future*, 1981.
8   Contemporary plans and descriptions of Coleshill appear in Morton, J.C., *The Farmer's Calendar*, 1862, p. 77; *The Builder*, 23 December 1854, pp. 653-5.
9   Dean, G.A., 'On the cost of agricultural buildings', *JRASE*, 1850, pp. 558-73.
10 Dean, G.A., *Essays on the Construction of Farm Buildings and Labourers' Cottages*, 1849.
11 See plan in Dean, G.A., *A series of Selected Designs for Country Residences, Entrance Lodges, Farm Offices, Cottages etc.*, 1867.
12 Denton, J. Bailey, *The Farm Homesteads of England*, 1863; the opening lines of the preface.
13 Figures quoted in Orwin, C.S., and Whetham, E.H., *History of British Agriculture 1846-1914*, 1964, p. 196.
14 See Spring, David, *The English Landed Estate in the Nineteenth Century: its Administration*, 1963, chapter 2.
15 Wade-Martins, Susanna, *A Great Estate at Work*, 1980.
16 Spring, David, *The English Landed Estate in the Nineteenth Century: its Administration*, 1963, p. 49.
17 Clarke, A.D., *Modern Farm Buildings: their Construction and Arrangement*, 3rd ed., 1899, p. 3.
18 Scott, J., *Farm Buildings with Plans and Estimates*, 1890, p. 5.

CHAPTER 2 : THE VICTORIAN FARM AT WORK

1 Ritchie, R., *The Farm Engineer*, 1849, chapter 3.
2 Cunningham, James, *Designs for Farm Cottages and Steadings*, 1842.
3 Loch, James, *An Account of the Improvements on the Estates of the Marquess of Stafford*, 1820.
4 Described in Andrews, G.H., *Agricultural Engineering*, 1852.
5 Loudon, J.C., *Observations on Laying Out Farms in the Scotch Style, Adapted to England*, 1812.
6 See *The Builder*, 21 July 1855, p.340.
7 See Morton, J.C., *The Farmer's Calendar*, 1862, p.89; also Spearing, J.B., 'On the agriculture of Berkshire', *JRASE*, 1860, p.31.
8 Morton, J.C., *The Farmer's Calendar*, 1862, p.95.
9 Copland, Samuel, *Agriculture, Ancient and Modern*, 1866, p.307.
10 Ewart, John, 'On the construction of farm buildings', *JRASE*, 1850.
11 Records of the Englefield estate in Berkshire Record Office, Ref. D/EBy E101.
12 Denton, J. Bailey, *The Farm Homesteads of England*, 1863, pp.57–9.
13 Morton, J.C., *Cyclopaedia of Agriculture*, 1855, Vol. 1, p.795.
14 Andrews, G.H., *Agricultural Engineering*, 1852, Vol. 2, p.148.
15 See *Illustrated London News*, 12 December 1857, p.585.
16 Denton, J. Bailey, *The Farm Homesteads of England*, 1863, p.23.
17 See, for example, Scott, John, *Farm Buildings: A Practical Treatise*, 1890.

CHAPTER 3 : DAIRY FARMS

1 Blundell, J.H., 'The Berkshire Farm Prize Competition, *JRASE*, 1882, p.542.
2 See Sheldon, J.P., *Dairy Farming*, 1878, p.xxi.
3 Description of farm in Denton, J. Bailey, *Farm Homesteads of England*, 1863, p.76.
4 See, for example, Denton, J. Bailey, *Farm Homesteads of England*, 1863, p.70, and Sheldon, J.P., *Dairy Farming*, 1878, p.85.
5 Morton, J.C., *The Prince Consort's Farms*, 1863, p.90.
6 'Jerseys at Buckhold', *Country Life*, 15 November 1902, p.636.
7 Voelcker, Dr Augustus, 'On Milk', *JRASE*, 1863, p.38.
8 Loudon, J.C., *An Encyclopaedia of Agriculture*, 2nd ed., 1831, p.1133.
9 Harding, Joseph, 'On the construction and heating of dairy and cheese rooms', *JRASE*, 1868, p.307.
10 Bowen-Jones, J., 'Report of the Somersetshire Farm Prize Competition, 1875' *JRASE*, 1875, p.529; also Gibbons, George, 'The practice of Cheddar cheese making', *JRASE*, 1889, pp.419–26.
11 White, Henry, 'A detailed account of the making of Cheshire cheese', *JRASE*,

1845, p. 102.

12 Rigby, Joseph, 'The practice of Cheshire cheese making', *JRASE*, 1889, pp. 427–37.

13 Bowen-Jones, J., 'Typical farms in Cheshire and North Wales', *JRASE*, 1893, p. 595.

14 ibid., p. 586.

15 ibid., p. 606.

16 ibid., p. 592.

CHAPTER 4 : FARMHOUSES AND COTTAGES

1 Waistell, Charles, *Designs for agricultural buildings*, 1827.

2 Goodwin, Francis, *Rural Architecture: Series of Designs for Rustic, Peasants' and Ornamental Cottages, Lodges and Villas, in Various Styles of Architecture*, 2nd edn, 1835.

3 Loudon, J. C., *An Encyclopaedia of Cottage, Farm and Villa Architecture and Furniture*, preface to first edition, 1833.

4 Dean, G. A., *A Series of Selected Designs for Country Residences, Entrance Lodges, Farm Offices, Cottages etc.*, 1867, text accompanying plate 2.

5 Denton, G. Bailey, *The Farm Homesteads of England*, 1863, pp. 101–8.

6 See *The Builder*, 5 January 1878.

7 Jefferies, Richard, *Hodge and his Masters*, Vol. 1 (first published 1880), 1966 edn, p. 101.

8 *Commission on the Employment of Children, Young Persons and Women in Agriculture*, 1867, Appendix Part 1, Report by the Revd James Fraser, p. 36.

9 ibid. Evidence provided by the Revd. A. J. Hare, Docking, p. 155.

10 *Royal Commission on Labour, The Agricultural Labourer*, 1893, Vol. 5, Part 1, General Report by William Little, p. 89.

11 *Commission on the Employment of Children, Young Persons and Women in Agriculture*, 1867, Report by the Revd James Fraser, evidence submitted by the Revd. J. B. Winckworth, p. 154.

12 For example, *Report on the Sanitary Condition of the Labouring Population*, 1842, edited by Edwin Chadwick, and *Report on the Employment of Women and Children in Agriculture*, 1843.

13 Macvicar, J. Young, 'Labourers' cottages', *JRASE*, 1849, p. 400.

14 Burke, French, 'On cottage economy and cookery,' *JRASE*, 1842, p. 100.

15 Tenth Duke of Bedford, *The Story of a Great Agricultural Estate*, 1897, p. 82.

16 Seventh Duke of Bedford, 'On labourers' cottages', *JRASE*, 1849, pp. 185–95.

17 *Royal Commission on Labour, The Agricultural Labourer*, 1893, Vol. 1, Report by William Bear, p. 22.

18 Little, H. J., 'The agricultural labourer', *JRASE*, 1878, p. 779.

19 The Revd Copinger Hill, 'On the construction of cottages', *JRASE*, 1843,

p. 356; Isaac, T. W. P., 'On the construction of labourers' cottages, *JRASE*, 1856, p. 424; Hunt, George, 'On concrete as a building material for farm buildings', *JRASE*, 1874, p. 211.

20 Denton, J. Bailey, *The Farm Homesteads of England*, 1863, p. 114.

21 Tenth Duke of Bedford, *The Story of a Great Agricultural Estate*, 1897, p. 95.

22 Lady Wantage, *Lord Wantage, V.C., K.C.B.; A Memoir*, 1907, p. 391.

23 See also Havinden, M. A., *Estate Villages*, 1966, for a study of the villages of Ardington and Lockinge.

24 Haggard, H. Rider, *Rural England*, Vol. 1 (first published 1902), 1906 edn, pp. 362-4.

CHAPTER 5 : LIVESTOCK

1 Karkeek, W. F., 'On the farming of Cornwall', *JRASE*, 1845, p. 449.

2 Corringham, R. W., 'Agriculture in Nottinghamshire', *JRASE*, 1845, p. 19.

3 Keary, Hall W., 'Management of cattle', *JRASE*, 1848, p. 426.

4 See Nicholls, George, 'On box feeding with linseed compounds', *JRASE*, 1847, pp. 473-87.

5 'The Broad Hinton herd', *The Farmer's Magazine*, May 1860, pp. 382-6.

6 See 'Mr Deane Willis's Shorthorns', *Country Life*, 12 July 1902, pp. 37-9.

7 Low David, *The breeds of the domestic animals of the British Islands*, 1842, p. 19.

8 'Mr Cridlan's Aberdeen-Angus herd', *Country Life*, 2 August 1902, pp. 136-8.

9 'Jerseys at Buckhold', *Country Life*, 22 November 1902, p. 650.

10 Rowlandson, T., 'On the breeds of sheep best adapted to different localities', *JRASE*, 1849, p. 435.

11 Jonas Webb describing his early life in *The Farmer's Magazine*, March, 1845, p. 196.

12 Howard, James, 'Pigs: their breeding and management', *JRASE*, 1881, p. 209.

13 See Pidgeon, Dan, 'Cold storage: its principles, practice and possibilities', *JRASE*, 1896, pp. 601-17.

CHAPTER 6 : FARM EQUIPMENT

1 Caird, James, *The Landed Interest and the Supply of Food*, 1878, p. 47.

2 Sturt, George, *The Wheelwright's Shop* (first published 1923), 1958 edn. p. 67.

3 ibid., p. 67.

4 Palin, William, 'The farming of Cheshire', *JRASE*, 1844, p. 83.

5 Ransome, J. Allen, *The Implements of Agriculture*, 1843, p. 16.

6 Dickinson, William, 'On the farming of Cumberland', *JRASE*, 1852, p. 240.

7 Parkes, Josiah, Legard, George, and Graburn, R. S., 'Report on the exhibition of implements at Liverpool', *JRASE*, 1841, p. ciii.

8 See Pidgeon, Dan, 'The development of agricultural machinery', *JRASE*, 1890, p. 263.

9 'Report on the exhibition and trial of implements at the Chelmsford Meeting, 1856', *JRASE*, 1856, p. 579.

10 Clarke, John Algernon, 'Report on the trials of steam-cultivating machinery at Wolverhampton', *JRASE*, 1871, p. 472.

11 Clarke J. A., 'Report of the second Inspection Committee enquiring into steam cultivation', *JRASE*, 1867, pp. 361–6.

12 Hall, Charles P., 'Miscellaneous implements exhibited at Cardiff', *JRASE*, 1901, p. 191.

CHAPTER 7 : THE AGRICULTURAL ENGINEERS

1 Morrison, Jean, 'R. & J. Reeves – Agricultural Implement Makers', *Wiltshire Folklife*, vol. 1, no. 1, (Autumn 1976).

2 Records of R. & J. Reeves in the Institute of Agricultural History and Museum of English Rural Life, University of Reading, TR REE MP1/2 Drill Register.

3 See the Records of R. Hunt & Co in the Institute of Agricultural History and Museum of English Rural Life, University of Reading.

4 *Implement and Machinery Review*, 1 February 1888, p. 10275.

5 Grace, D. R., and Phillips, D. C., *Ransomes of Ipswich*, 1975.

6 'The Orwell Works of Messrs Ransomes, Sims and Jefferies', *The Engineer*, 30 July 1886, pp. 94–5.

7 'The Leiston Works in Suffolk', *The Engineer* 2 December 1870, p. 379.

8 'Clayton & Shuttleworth, Stamp End Works, Lincoln', *Implement and Machinery Review*, 1 September 1897, p. 21964.

9 'Up to date threshing machines and boilers', *Implement and Machinery Review*, 2 November 1900, p. 25920.

10 Thompson, H. S., 'Report on the exhibition and trial of implements at the York Meeting, 1848', *JRASE*, Vol. 9, 1848, p. 407.

11 'Visit of Indian and colonial exhibition delegates to the Spittlegate Works, Grantham,' *Implement and Machinery Review*, 1 August 1886, p. 8537.

12 Howard, James, 'Pigs; and experience in their breeding and management', *JRASE*, 1881, pp. 205–20.

13 'Mr James Howard', *The Farmer's Magazine*, January 1860, p. 4.

14 'The Britannia Ironworks', *The Engineer*, 16 September 1870, pp. 187–8.

CHAPTER 8 : UNLOCKING THE SECRETS OF SCIENTIFIC AGRICULTURE

1 Pusey, Philip, 'On the present state of the science of agriculture in England', *JRASE*, vol. 1, 1840, pp. 1–21.
2 Paynter, John, 'On gas-water as a manure', *JRASE*, vol. 1, 1840, p. 45.
3 See Caird, James, *English Agriculture 1850–51*, 1852, p. 112.
4 Mechi, J. J., *How to Farm Profitably*, 6th edn, 1860.
5 Caird, James, *English Agriculture 1850–51*, 1852, p. 141.
6 Burritt, Elihu, *A Walk from London to John o'Groats*, 1864, p. 25.
7 Morton, John, *On the Nature and Property of Soils*, 2nd edn, 1840, p. 252.
8 Both are included in the 4th edn of *On the Nature and Property of Soils*, 1842. The project has also been very well described in Dr Celia Miller's 'Whitfield Example Farm: a Victorian model', *Bristol Industrial Archaeology Society Journal*, 16, 1983.
9 Daubeny, Charles, 'The application of science to agriculture', *JRASE*, 1842, pp. 136–59.
10 Lawes, John Bennet, 'On agricultural chemistry', *JRASE*, 1847, p. 226.
11 ibid., p. 245.
12 See Voelcker, J. Augustus, 'The Woburn Experimental Farm', *JRASE*, 1897, part 1, pp. 258–293, part 2, pp. 622–55.
13 Lawrence, Charles 'The Royal Agricultural College of Cirencester', *JRASE*, 1865, p. 3.
14 Caird, James, *English Agriculture 1850–51*, 1852, p. 39.

CHAPTER 9 : FARMS FOR AN INDUSTRIAL AGE

1 Buckland, George, 'On the farming of Kent', *JRASE*, 1845, pp. 251–303.
2 Charnock, John, 'On the farming of the W. Riding of Yorkshire', *JRASE*, 1848, pp. 284–311.
3 Rigby, Thomas, 'Report on the Farm Prize Competition in Northumberland and Durham; Class 4 and 5', *JRASE*, 1888, pp. 224–42.
4 Clarke, J. A., 'Farming of Lincolnshire', *JRASE*, 1851, p. 328.
5 From an essay on sewage manure, dated March 1853, published in the second edition of J. J. Mechi, *How to Farm Profitably*, 1860, pp. 100–6.
6 See 'Town sewage', *JRASE*, 1867, pp. 467–95.
7 See 'Report of the judges on the Sewage Farm Competition, 1879', *JRASE*, 1880, pp. 1–79; also Morton, John Chalmers, 'Half a dozen English sewage farms', *JRASE*, 1876, pp. 407–39.
8 Bear, William, 'The food supply of Manchester: 1. vegetable produce', *JRASE*, 1897, p. 212.

9   Bear, William, 'Flower & fruit farming in England', *JRASE*, 1889, p. 30.

10 See Sheldon, J.P., *Dairy Farming*, 1878, pp. 252–83.

11 Jenkins, H.M., 'Report on the practice of ensilage at home and abroad', *JRASE*, 1884, pp. 126–246.

12 Goffart, Auguste, *Manuel de la culture et de l'ensilage des Maïs et autres fourrages verts*, 1877.

13 See Potter, Thomas, *The Construction of Silos*, 1886, pp. 81–3.

14 Privy Council Office, *Return of the Replies to Questions Relating to Silos and Ensilage*, 1885, and *Report of the Ensilage Commissioners*, 1886.

15 See Scott, John, *Farm Buildings – A Practical Treatise*, 1890, pp. 62–74.

16 Amos, Arthur, 'Ensilage', *Journal of the Farmers' Club*, March 1920.

17 See Burritt, Elihu, *A Walk from London to John o' Groats*, 1864, pp. 163–83.

18 Haggard, H. Rider, *Rural England*, Vol. 1, 1906 edn, pp. 527–33.

19 ibid., p. 528.

20 Orwin, C.S., *Progress in English Farming Systems: III A Specialist in Arable Farming*, 1930.

Index

Index

superphosphate, 197–8, 232

Tancred, Sir Thomas, 27
Technical Instruction Act (1888), 208
tenant farmers, 39, 41, 50
tithe, 16
Thompson, H.S., 27
threshing machine, 25, 32, 36, 46, 47, 48, 50, 62, 148, **154**, 175, **176**
Torrington, Lord, 25
tramways, engineering, 176, **186**
Turnbull, J.R., 75, 83
Tyne & Wear, Bowes House Farm, Lambton, 211; Over the Hill Farm, Houghton-le-Spring, 211

Union, Agricultural Labourers', 114
universities, 209

vegetables, 219–20
Voelcker, Dr Augustus, 78, 203, 230, 232

wagon, **142**, 143, **235**
Waistell, Charles, 93

Waite, Richard, **42**
Wantage, Lord, 112–13
Warwickshire, Heathcote Farm, Leamington Spa, **216**, 217
water meadows, 189–90
water power, **21**, 48–50, 62, 99
Watney, Dr Herbert, 77, **129**
Webb, Jonas, 131–55
Wedlake, 48
Westminster, Duke of, 89–90
Wilkin, A.C., 220
Wilkinson, William, 66, 67, 68
Willis, Deane, 123–5, **125**
Wiltshire, Bapton Manor, 123–5, **125**; Bemerton Farm, Wilton, 72; Broad Hinton, 122–4, **124**; Longleat Home Farm, 57, 59, 68; Netherhampton Farm, Wilton, 41
wind power, farm, 46; for fen drainage, 211
Worcestershire, Croome Court estate, 115, 220

Yorkshire, Manor Farm, Catterick, 48